C000232174

# Contents

**INDEX ON CENSORSHIP**

VOLUME 43 NUMBER 03

AUTUMN 2014

# Culture

92-94 TOOLEY STREET, LONDON SE1 2TH

EDITOR
RACHAEL JOLLEY
DEPUTY EDITOR
VICKY BAKER
SUB EDITOR
PAUL ANDERSON, SALLY GIMSON
CONTRIBUTING EDITORS:
KAYA GENC (TURKEY), NATASHA JOSEPH
(SOUTH AFRICA), JEMIMAH STENFIELD

EDITORIAL ASSISTANT:
Alice Kirkland
THANKS TO: Sean Gallagher, Milana Knes-
sevic, Matthew Hasteley, Brett Biedscheid

Supported by
ARTS COUNCIL
ENGLAND

# Seeing the future of journalism and its power

*by* **Rachael Jolley**

**EDITORIAL**

43(3): 3/6 | DOI: 10.1177/0306422014550968

**IMAGINE THIS: A** journalist with his or her own personal news drone camera that can be sent to any coordinates in the world to film what is going on. Imagine a world where you had the ability to program a whole set of drone cameras to go and film a riot, a rally or a refugee camp.

Imagine being able to set off your smartphone in a plastic bottle down a dangerous river to take photos that might prove the river water is carrying disease or is not safe to drink. How about drone cameras that you can leash to your GPS co-ordinates to follow and film you or someone else? Those worlds should not be hard to imagine as they exist (or are being built) already, and, in some cases, are already being used by journalists.

The future of journalism is going to build on technologies we already have. But we must remember it isn't really about the technology, but about what it can help us deliver. When the subject of the future of journalism is discussed it often turns to whizzy gadgets but the debate about whether the public ends up being better informed and better equipped happens less often.

The information superhighway, as the internet was once called, was supposed to give individuals amazing access to knowledge that they couldn't access before, from historical documents to live video footage. And it has.

But the thing that most of us didn't bargain for was that it would mean we had so much stuff coming at us. We no longer knew where to turn, our eyes and ears were full, a welter of "news" snippets became impossible to absorb, and as for analysis, well, who had time for that?

The reality of exciting new technology is that it is coming to the market at a time when the public appears to value journalists less, and can turn to Twitter or Facebook or citizen journalists to find out what's going on in the world. Journalists; who needs them when we can find out so much for ourselves? It's a reasonable question, and of course good and determined researchers can find out plenty of information for themselves, if they have hours to spend. But then again journalists have a whole set of tools and training that should mean they are better than the average member of the public at finding out facts and analysing reports as well as presenting the end results.

Journalists are trained and practiced at interviewing, asking the right questions and drawing out relevant pieces of information. These are rarely acknowledged skills but you have only to switch on a phone-in programme or watch a set of →

ABOVE: A man takes a photo of a protest in Tahrir Square, Egypt

parliamentarians try to quiz a witness at a committee to know asking a good question is not as easy as it might seem. Knowing where to look for evidence and sources is not always so simple as putting any old question into Google either. Then there is analysing charts, graphs and tables; this is becoming a particularly valued set of skills. When it comes to recognising a story, then the good old reporter's nose comes in handy. And writing up and compiling a story so that it makes sense and tells the story well is perhaps the most underrated skill of all. Good writing is sadly underappreciated.

With a toolkit like that, it is not surprising that governments around the world would rather journalists weren't at the scene of a demonstration, or sharpening up their introduction of a story about a government cover-up. Perhaps that's why governments around the world from the USA to China make it especially difficult, or particularly expensive, for journalists to get a visa. And that's why journalists are targeted, watched, held captive, and in some horrific cases, such as with US journalist James Foley, murdered. Increasingly journalists are working on a freelance basis from war zones and conflicts. As our writer Iona Craig reports from Yemen, this can leave you exposed on two levels – without the protection of being a staff member of a huge news organisation, and without any income if you can't file stories. That exposure to pressure, and possible violence, also affects bloggers operating as reporters, and is something that worries OSCE's Dunja Mijatovic (interviewed in this issue), who is trying to bring journalists from different countries together in Vienna this month to discuss what needs to be done.

Journalists are still needed by societies, what they do can be very important (although sometimes very trivial too). At the same time that job is changing. In this issue Raymond Joseph's fascinating article shows how African newsrooms with little money are able to use low-cost technology such as remote-controlled drone cameras to monitor oil spills, as well as less-sexy-sounding data analysis tools to help reporters find out what is going on. He also reports on how newsrooms are working closely with citizen reporters to bring news from regions that were previously unreported. Work being carried out by Naija Voices in Nigeria, and by our Index 2014 award winner Shu Choudhary in India, shows how technology can help augment old-fashioned reporting, getting news to and from remote areas.

News reporting is also taking different forms to reach different audiences, as was brought home to me at the Film Forward conference in Malmö, Sweden, this summer, when US journalist Nonny de la Peña and Danish journalist Steven Achiam showed the audience how interactive news "games" and cartoon-style films are new forms of reportage. Achiam's Deadline Athen is a journalism game that allows the player to become a journalist in Athens, collecting information about a riot and shows the choices that are available; it gives the players options of where to find out and source the story.

## These pioneering approaches so far only have small audiences compared to TV news

La Peña uses her journalistic skills to engage "players" in the experience of being imprisoned in Guantanamo Bay, using real news sources to inform what the "player" experiences so that it is similar to what prisoners experienced. Both Achiam and La Peña argue that these type of approaches will engage and inform different audiences in finding out about the world, audiences that would not be minded to read a newspaper or watch the TV news.

There's not yet a journalism ethics handbook that covers these approaches. Both La Peña and Achiam are award-winning journalists and have merged their existing set of research skills with a different style. Both talk about sourcing information for their news films, and La Peña offers links to evidence for her virtual-reality storytelling.

These pioneering approaches so far only have small audiences compared to TV news, but will undoubtedly challenge journalists of the future to learn new skills (video and animation look increasingly like core modules).

Interviewing, research and legal knowledge are always going to part of the mix; they are the skills that give journalists the tools to find out what others would rather they didn't. And that skill package is always going to be vital. ☒

© Rachael Jolley
www.indexoncensorship.org

**Rachael Jolley** is editor of Index on Censorship

# 33rd İSTANBUL INTERNATIONAL

100 YEARS OF CINEMA IN TURKEY

## NOVEMBER 8-16, 2014

ULUSLARARASI SALON 8-11 KASIM
INTERNATIONAL HALL NOVEMBER 8-11

**MACARİSTAN**
ONUR KONUĞU
**HUNGARY**
GUEST OF HONOR
**Bir Bahçeden Bir Bahçeye**
Egyik Kertből Másikba
*From One Garden to the Other*

*www.istanbulbookfair.com*

kitapfuari

istanbulkitapfuari

kitapfuari

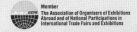
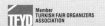

İSTANBUL

**TÜYAP FAIR CONVENTION AND CONGRESS CENTER**
Büyükçekmece, İstanbul / Turkey

*IS FAIR IS HELD UPON THE AUTHORIZATION OF THE UNION OF CHAMBERS AND COMMODITY EXCHANGES OF TURKEY,*
*IN ACCORDANCE WITH LAW NUMBER 5174.*

ABOVE: Reporters in Yemen face challenges from the security forces as they research stories. Police and army troopers patrol a street in Sana'a

SPECIAL REPORT

## In this section

# Back to the future

43(3): 8/12 | DOI: 10.1177/0306422014548392

Journalists in war zones may need to ignore technology and go back to old ways of avoiding surveillance, says award-winning foreign correspondent **Iona Craig**

IT WAS AROUND 10pm somewhere between the town of Seiyun and the drone-strike hot spot of al-Qatn in Yemen's eastern province of Hadhramaut. We were on the run from Yemeni security forces. After being on the road for 15 hours, we were also out of fuel.

Westerners have been banned from travelling to Hadhramaut since 2012. Almost as soon as we arrived in Seiyun in the north of the province last September, after a seven-hour drive from the city of Mukalla on Yemen's southern coast, I managed to get on the wrong side of the regional head of security. It was then I realised we had a choice: flee or face arrest. I chose the former.

As our small party of three – me, the driver Ibrahim (a pseudonym to protect his

## Encrypted email is now a basic requirement and simple counter surveillance measures are essential tools

identity) plus my friend and fellow journalist, Shuaib al-Mosawa – bolted, I ordered all phones switched off and batteries and SIM cards removed. We had multiple military checkpoints to get through. There was little point in skulking through the night, me as a Yemeni woman covered head to toe in a black *abiya* and all-concealing *niqab* face veil, with Shuaib and Ibrahim as my male "relatives", only to give our location away to either a passing drone, or Yemen's intelligence agency, the US-backed National Security Bureau (NSB).

It is a given in Yemen that the NSB listens in to the telephone conversations of all journalists. But, if the false trail we had left worked, they should think we were tucked up in our hotel beds rather than hunting for petrol in the middle of the night before retracing our steps and heading back on the road south.

Today, the most persistent threat to journalists in conflict zones is as likely to be from government agencies, often, such as Yemen's NSB, possibly with the active assistance of government agencies of the foreign nations we hail from.

Whether you are in the middle of the desert in Yemen, on the streets of Cairo or in your home in Texas, as the American journalist Barrett Brown learnt, if your reporting is critical of the state, or you just dig too deep, you are inviting the wrath of government authorities. The consequences can vary, from jail, through deportation and being added to a government blacklist, to threats on your life.

Not wanting to doze off and leave Ibrahim driving alone, and once I knew enough miles were between us and our unwanted trackers, my mind started to wander towards money. I began calculating in my head what our run-in with northern Hadhramaunt's security director was going to cost. Two to three bits of work lost and a pointless 14-hour drive through the desert made it an expensive error.

As a freelance, with no one to cover expenses, you pay dearly for mistakes when local security forces prevent you from doing your job. Aside from the threat posed by being caught, a particular danger for my Yemeni travelling companions, I would pay out my own pocket for the blunder.

Shuaib's day rate for translation, and the pitiful amount Ibrahim was charging for driving us in his taxi almost the full length of eastern Yemen and back, made this a US$450 excursion with nothing to show for it.

The stories I would have written from these three days' work would have more than covered my costs, but now I was left with empty hands and empty pockets.

I cursed myself, then the security director who had kicked up all the fuss and sent his soldiers after us, and then the state of an industry that had me, as a consequence of the lost income, working at somewhere under five US cents an hour for my troubles; troubles which still included the very real possibility of all three of us being arrested. We were also breaking one of my golden rules in Yemen: never travel in remote rural areas by night. Even if we avoided being detected by the security forces, a drone strike on the road back was not implausible, nor was being ambushed.

From the back seat I tapped Ibrahim on the shoulder and only half-joking said: "Don't drive behind any other vehicles. Especially not any Suzuki Vitaras" – the regular vehicle of choice of Yemen's al-Qaeda militants. He smiled a leafy-green, qat-filled grin – qat is the mild narcotic plant chewed by the majority of Yemenis whose stimulating effect was essential to get Ibrahim through the night's drive without falling asleep at the wheel. "If we find Nasser al-Wuhayshi do we get a reward?" he chuckled, referring to the infamous leader of Al-Qaeda in the Arabian Peninsula (AQAP).

Governments going after journalists is nothing new. But what is increasingly apparent is that those listening and watching when we work in countries infamous for their consistent stifling of freedom of speech and obstruction of a free press, are often doing so with the infrastructure, equipment or direct support of supposedly "liberal" Western nations.

As reports by the online news platform The Intercept, set up by Glenn Greenwald and Laura Poitras, note: "The US government shares its watchlist data with local law enforcement, foreign governments, and 'private entities'." Once the US government secretly labels you a terrorist suspect, other institutions tend to treat you as one.

In Yemen there has been occasions when journalists and activists have fallen into the "terrorist suspect" category. Washington's involvement in keeping Yemeni journalist Abdulelah Haider Shaye – jailed for three years until his release in July last year – was revealed in information, released by the White House in February 2011, that detailed a phone call between the US president and his Yemeni counterpart during which President Barack Obama expressed his "concern" at his pending release. Consequently Shaye remained in solitary confinement for another two and a half years.

Last September Baraa Shiban, the local representative for Reprieve, who has extensively gathered evidence from US drone strikes in Yemen, was held under the 200 Terrorism Act at Gatwick Airport while he was on his way to speak alongside me at a Chatham House event. We were due to share a panel discussion on, ironically, Yemen's security.

It would be naive to assume that the list of journalists and activists who have ended up on America's extensive watchlist would only include these two individuals. Though Western states like to stand on the moral

# A US drone buzzing over your head while you interview drone-strike survivors reminds you who is watching

high ground, the US government's example to the world on how to deal with journalists who seek to challenge the official narrative is far from exemplary.

Under the current administration the United States "model" has seen Obama's justice department directing a record number of prosecutions relating to leaked information. It emerged last year that the phone records of 20 Associated Press journalists were secretly obtained as part of an investigation into apparent unauthorised leaked information used in a March 2012 story about a spy in AQAP who foiled a terrorist plot.

In Yemen, if strange sounds on your phone line are not enough to heighten your paranoia, a US drone buzzing continuously over your head while you interview drone-strike survivors and victims' family members – as →

→ happened to me on one reporting trip last year – should be enough to remind you who is watching and who you should be afraid of.

In addition to the surveillance tactics, the rush for control and manipulation of information has reached a frenzy under Obama. Thanks to Edward Snowden's revelations we know that Britain's agencies have also played a significant role in the manipulation and falsifying of information, or "the art of deception" as British intelligence agency Government Communications Headquarters (GCHQ) called it, in order, as the journalist Glenn Greenwald noted in his reporting, "to control, infiltrate, manipulate, and warp online discourse".

## Until encrypted mobile phone communication becomes more affordable and commonplace, we may have to go back in time – meeting in person rather than leaving a data trail

Mitigating the risks posed by government surveillance and attempts to control information is not expensive, compared to buying a flak jacket, or paying for hostile environment training, which gets editors and penny-pinching media organisations off the hook.

Primarily the onus falls on the journalists to judge how sensitively their communications – whether by phone, email or other increasingly popular social media tools such as WhatsApp – need to be handled. A balance has to be found between a disregard for communications security and histrionic paranoia when it comes to the clandestine threat.

But being caught in the middle of a firefight, a journalist is going to be much more conscious of being exposed without body armour and a helmet than when he or she is on GChat exchanging information with a source or discussing reporting plans with an editor via email without encryption. What should not be forgotten when working in conflict zones is that the hidden threat of government surveillance is as real as the visible one from bombs and bullets.

Technology, even something as simple as a mobile phone, makes journalists' jobs easier. But it also makes the job easier for governments who seek to control and surveil us. One of the many things we can learn from the Snowden files is that doing nothing to protect our sources and ourselves from intelligence agencies will, in turn, make all our jobs more difficult. By discounting the need to change the way we work and carrying on regardless we play into the hands of governments who benefit from knowing much more about us and our activities when we are trying to find out more about theirs.

For now, until encrypted mobile phone communication becomes more affordable and commonplace, we may have to go back in time – meeting in person rather than leaving a data trail behind us. Failing that encrypted email is now a basic requirement and simple counter surveillance measures are essential tools.

As the gallows humour mantra of today's journalists, taken from the 1970 film adaptation of Joseph Heller's Catch 22, goes: "Just because you're paranoid doesn't mean they aren't after you." ☒

© Iona Craig
www.indexoncensorship.org

**Iona Craig** was The Times correspondent in Yemen 2010-2014. She regularly writes for Index and was recently awarded the Martha Gelhorn prize. She tweets @ionacraig

# Digital detectives

43(3): 13/16 | DOI: 10.1177/0306422014547845

Easy-to-use technology is helping investigative journalists across Africa carry out research, even on small budgets, finds **Raymond Joseph**

**D**EEP IN MPUMALANGA province, in the far north-east of South Africa, a poorly resourced newspaper is using a combination of high and low tech solutions to make a difference in the lives of the communities it serves.

It is also pioneering a new and innovative form of journalism that not only places its readers at the centre of its coverage, but also involves them directly in the newsgathering operation.

What this small newspaper does is a lesson for bigger, more established media outlets, which are searching for new non-traditional revenue streams and which, in the age of online and digital journalism, struggle to survive and remain relevant.

The Ziwaphi community-based newspaper is distributed to communities in the Nkomazi district, situated at the epicentre of the South Africa AIDS pandemic, where there is very little access to news reporting. One of the biggest problems in the area is water contaminated with sewage. Women and young girls spend hours every day collecting water from rivers for drinking, cooking and washing, but these same rivers are also often used to dispose of human waste. As a result the E.coli count sometimes spikes, causing diarrhoea. And every few years, there is an outbreak of cholera.

Using a grant, and technology assistance from the African Media Initiative (AMI), which is spearheading the drive to embed data-driven journalism in African newsrooms, Ziwaphi is placing old smartphones submerged in clear plastic bottles in rivers in the area. Functioning as simple electron microscopes, the phones use their cameras to take regular flash-lit pictures. These photographs are then magnified and compared against images from an existing database to detect dangerous levels of E.coli. The results are delivered via SMS to residents, informing them where it's safe to collect water.

Completing the circle, the newspaper analyses the real-time data to detect trends, and hopefully even triangulates the sources of contamination.

Once a month, Ziwaphi publishes an in-depth story based on the results, which is shared with other community papers and local radio stations in the area. The hope is the information can then empower ordinary people in the region to force the government to deliver clean water and sanitation. Ziwaphi's readers also help gather information themselves using a mobile-based citizen reporting app which supplements the smartphone data with eyewitness stories about the impacts of the pollution, and possible sources of contamination.

"The total project only cost $20 000, including a modest salary for a year for a full-time health reporter," says Justin Arenstein, a strategist for AMI. "But the important thing, from a media sustainability perspective, is that Ziwaphi is using →

ABOVE: Quadcopters, like this one flown by Ben Kreimer of the University of Nebraska's Drone Journalism Lab, are being used by African SkyCam to collect images

cables is helping bring down the cost of connectivity, especially in east and southern Africa. This has sparked an exciting new era for journalism, with an explosion of ideas and innovations that are producing "news you can use" tools. Established media is increasingly reaching out to citizens to involve them in their news-gathering and content production processes. The phone-in-a-bottle project is an example of what can be done with limited resources.

In Kenya, the Radio Group, the third largest media house, has set up Star Health, the first in a set of toolkits to help readers do easy background checks on doctors and learn whether they have ever been found guilty of malpractice. In one case a man working as a doctor turned out to be a vet.

The site, which has proved to be a big hit in a country where dodgy doctors are a major problem, also helps users locate medical specialists and their nearest health facility. It can also be used to check whether medicines are covered by the national health scheme. Importantly, the results of queries on Star Health are delivered via a premium SMS service that generates an income stream, crucial in an age when media needs to diversify revenue models away from reliance on advertising and, in some case, copy sales.

"These tools don't replace traditional journalism, rather they augment journalistic reportage by, for example, helping readers to find out how a national story on dodgy doctors personally affects them," says Arenstein. News must be personal and actionable and should become an important part of the media's digital transformation strategies, he stresses.

The reality of journalism today is that, even though outlets may not have the large audiences of conventional media, anyone with a smartphone or basic digital skills has the ability to be a "publisher".

In Nigeria, for example, the Sahara online community has over a million followers on

→ the water project to build the digital backbone it will need to survive in the near future."

# Drones and camera-equipped balloons help media that cannot afford news helicopters to collect footage for stories

Until recently Africa lagged behind the rest of the world where the internet was concerned, because of the high cost of access. But now the deployment of new undersea

social media, far more than many media houses. The challenge in the future will be for newsrooms to tap into these grassroots networks, but still keep citizens' voices at their centre.

A pioneering project in Nigeria's isolated Delta region has seen the mainstream media working with an existing citizen-reporting network, Naija Voices, to adopt remote-controlled drones fitted with cameras to monitor for environmentally destructive oil spills. The plan is to syndicate the footage to mainstream TV and newspaper partners in Lagos and Abuja. This would allow the newspapers unprecedented reach into parts of the country that had previously been largely inaccessible.

The fixed-wing drones are relatively cheap and simple to fly, but they crash from time to time. "Getting new parts, like the wings or pieces of the fuselage, would be costly and time consuming, so we're experimenting with 3D printers to create parts onsite and on demand," says Arenstein.

This citizen-reporting experiment builds on the work of AfricaSkyCam which for the past year has been experimenting with drones in Kenya as part of "Africa's first newsroom-based eye-in-the-sky". SkyCam uses drones and camera-equipped balloons to help media that cannot afford news helicopters to cover breaking news in dangerous situations or difficult to reach locations.

In South Africa, Oxpeckers Center for Investigative Environmental Reporting is using "geo journalism" and other mapping techniques to amplify its reporting and to analyse stories such as rhino poaching and canned lion hunting – breeding tame lions for wealthy trophy-hunters to shoot. Investigations help uncover trends or links to criminal syndicates and the Oxpeckers Center's reportage is credited with promoting a recent ban on canned hunting in Botswana, and helping to shape laws on trade in rhino and other wildlife products in China and in Mozambique.

But the reality is that poorly resourced African newsrooms seldom have the in-house technology or digital skills to build new online tools.

So, AMI's digital innovation programme and similar initiatives at Google, the Bill & Melinda Gates Foundation, and at smaller donors including the Indigo Trust are all building external support systems to help newsrooms leapfrog into a digital future.

Donors are also focusing on embedding data journalism approaches into mainstream media. They are helping journalists use publicly available digital information from sources such as censuses or government

# We are experimenting with 3D printers to create parts on site for remote-controlled drones fitted with cameras

budgets to build decision-making tools to help ordinary citizens make better informed decisions on bread and butter issues affecting their lives.

Helping drive the new-tech approach is Code for Africa, a network of civic technology labs planned for countries across the continent to help drive innovation and to work with media and citizen journalist networks, to help them bridge the digital divide.

Code for South Africa (C4SA) is helping everyone, from the township-based Ziwaphi and its cholera alert project, to national media outlets, such as the Mail & Guardian and City Press.

"The media know they're in crisis, with their advertising-based business model under threat as audiences shift online, but digital innovation is still a hard sell," says C4SA director Adi Eyal. "Progress is painstakingly slow because many African media owners are hesitant to invest before they know how these new models will generate revenue. →

→ The result is that much of what South African newsrooms are calling home-grown data journalism is just visualisation. They're creating very little actionable information and virtually no news tools that people can use to make decisions. The investment in a one-off project is high, so it is important that the tools that are built live on, so that newsrooms can use them to report on issues and people can act."

Progress is painstakingly slow, but nevertheless the building blocks are slowly being put in place as the "root stock" – datasets from across Africa – is collected and collated on the African Open Data portal for both newsroom journalists and civic coders to use. The data means they can create applications and tools which will help them build communities and generate income.

C4SA is also building an "invisible" back-end infrastructure that newsrooms can help build news tools quickly and cheaply. This includes support for initiatives such as OpenAfrica that helps newsrooms digitise and extract data from source documents. C4SA has also built a series of open, machine-readable, data rich application programming interfaces (APIs) that newsrooms can easily plug into their mobile apps or websites. The APIs drive tools like WaziMap, which uses censuses, elections and other data to help journalists to dig into the make up of communities, right down to local ward level. Each of these resources is a tool not only for the media, but also for civic activists and public watchdogs, says Arenstein.

In a recent column on the future of newspapers, Ferial Haffajee, the editor of City Press, a national South African Sunday newspaper that is struggling to reinvent itself in the digital age, wrote: "Nothing is as it was. Nor are most things what they seem. We have a future, and it is tantalising." And you just need to look at the smartphones in a bottle and 3D-printed drones to know that this future is slowly, newsroom by newsroom, project by project, becoming a reality. X

© Raymond Joseph
www.indexoncensorship.org

**Raymond Joseph** is a Cape Town-based freelance journalist. He is on the board of Big Issue, South Africa, and tweets @rayjoe

# RE-WRITING
# THE FUTURE

Credit: keepics / Alamy

Five young journalists write
from around the world
– Yemen, South Africa,
Germany, India and the Czech
Republic – on their concerns
and hopes for the profession

ABOVE: A young
journalist reporting
from Ottawa,
Canada

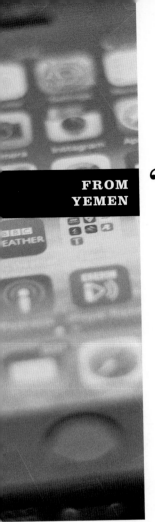

# "We can't counter propaganda with censorship"

43(3): 20/21 | DOI: 10.1177/0306422014550963

The Yemeni government should not be the ones judging the objectivity of reporting, but there is hope for more freedom, says **Ahlam Mohsen**

YEMEN FOUND ITSELF near the bottom of the list this year – yet again – for press freedom, ranking 167 out of 180 countries, according to the Press Freedom Index. Journalism in Yemen is full of contradictions. There may be less direct censorship under the coalition government, but there has been a surge of attacks on journalists and critics.

I arrived in Yemen – the country I was born in but hardly knew – from the US shortly after Yemen's president, Ali Abdul-

## Yemen is the only Arab country other than Jordan to pass an access to information law

lah Saleh, stepped down from office in early 2012. I was an activist at home and was struck by how in the US we could not manage to continue occupying a park, yet Yemen was bringing down a government.

After the Arab Spring in 2011, Yemeni journalists saw a number of victories, such as the passage of the Access to Information Law, which gave new hope for more transparency in government institutions. Yemen is

the only Arab country other than Jordan to pass such a law. But, like the brief blossoming of press freedom following unification in 1990, victories are not always permanent and progress is not necessarily linear.

For four months now, the newspaper where I work, the Yemen Times, has been trying to access the government's oil contracts with foreign and multinational corporations. We could go down the route of trying to access leaked documents, but it is important to receive them directly from the government, so we know the full terms – and also so future decisions will be fully transparent.

With an increase in newspapers, radios and television stations that are affiliated with and financed by various political parties and influential individuals, there is a real concern about the use of such media organisations to spread propaganda. Television channel Yemen Today was shut down by the government in June, after being accused of incitement against the current rulers during the country's fuel crisis.

Unusually, many critics of government censorship fell silent this time around, failing to condemn the move because the station belonged to the country's former dictator,

Saleh. But the move is an alarming one. By allowing the government to be the judge of what is and is not "objective" reporting, we are handing over a power that should rest solely with the public. We can't counter propaganda with censorship. The government needs to not only end censorship, but also to prosecute those who harass and attack journalists so they are not tempted to self-censor – by far a larger problem in the country than direct censorship.

Being a female journalist also presents its problems. I have seen young women rush out to cover a bombing or an assassination, knowing that though they may arrive first at the scene, soldiers will surround them and focus on their presence and safety, while they watch their male colleagues rush past them. The problem is a deep-rooted one, and is bound up with the future of women more broadly. But there is much to be hopeful about, as Yemen moves towards a 30 per cent quota of female representation in the government and women continue to assert their right to being in the public sphere.

Nothing is certain in Yemen. There could be many paths ahead, varying from a successful transition to democracy or possible civil war. Yet despite all the challenges and risks of reporting in Yemen, I am optimistic about the future. The Freedom of Information Act is a radical law, which, if followed, will give us the right to know almost everything our government does. If we can make this law meaningful by using it and not just having it as words on paper, journalists – and the public – have a lot to look forward to. ✕

© Ahlam Mohsen
www.indexoncensorship.org

ABOVE: Presenters at Yemen FM, a private radio station in Sana'a, April 2014

**Ahlam Mohsen**, 26, is a Yemeni-American writer living in Sana'a and is the deputy editor-in-chief of the Yemen Times

FROM
GERMANY

# "Journalism has never been more exciting"

43(3): 22/23 | DOI: 10.1177/0306422014550963

**Katharina Frick** did seven internships in Germany to kickstart her career, yet remains optimistic about new ways of funding the media

**I**N GERMANY, AS in many other places around the world, newsrooms are being shut down, advertising markets are at a low and the newspaper industry has lost nearly a quarter of circulation in the past decade. Why do I still want to become a journalist? Because it has never been more exciting.

I come from a family of journalists. My mum and dad have worked in the journalism and communication field almost their entire lives. Many things have changed from when they started working in the newsroom

## Amid a funding crisis, those with creative ideas and entrepreneurial skills come into play more than ever before

of a local daily newspaper over 30 years ago and they both agree that competition now is much stronger. My mum was hired on the spot for her first job, without any prior experience. This seems out of the question today. I did seven internships during my studies – some with low pay, some with no pay.

Half of these internships and jobs I got through contacts and connections, half

of them without. Good contacts seem to be more important than before and that is something that I have come to hate about the field. I have always wanted to achieve things on my own, but I have come to realise that it does not work that way. At least not if you want to get into big, traditional media houses.

That is why I am more and more tempted to focus on new and fresh approaches to media, where ideas and creativity are valued more than knowing someone, such as in a journalistic start-ups. Amid a funding crisis, those with creative ideas and entrepreneurial skills come into play more than ever before. I don't believe there is one solution to save the future of journalism; I think there are many. Now is the right time to experiment and try out business models with different financial models and content ideas.

In Germany, few readers are willing to pay for online articles, and only very few publishing houses have had the courage to experiment with payment models or pay walls. The daily newspaper Die Welt, for example, uses a "leaky pay wall", similar to the ones used by The New York Times and the UK's The Daily Telegraph, allowing users to read 20 articles on the same browser for free every month. The Süddeutsche Zeitung, one of Germany's largest dailies, just recently announced that it will introduce a similar model by the end of the year.

One innovative project that has recently succeeded in Germany is Krautreporter (as in crowd-reporter). It was started by 28 relatively renowned freelance journalists, who wanted to create an online publication filled with long-form stories, without only seeking clicks and without any advertising. So they asked the public for money. Their goal was €900,000 from 15,000 supporters in 30 days. Within the last hours of their crowd-funding period just enough people donated €60 each. In the end, over €1 million was raised, supposedly the biggest sum ever crowd-funded for a journalistic project in Germany. The journalists will each earn €2,000 to €2,500 per month, allowing them to fully engage in their research without constantly having to worry about the next assignment.

Instead of hiding every article behind a pay wall, Krautreporter will be accessible to all, but the €5-per-month fee will allow the users special privileges, such as commenting on articles, attending events and mixing with the journalists. Engaging and interacting with readers and users on such a level is something that is still new to most traditional media and many publishers are closely watching this reader-membership concept.

Of course, new projects hardly ever come along without disapproval. The Krautreporters were criticised for being vague about details and planned content in the early days, and for their selection of journalists (the majority being male and with no diversity in backgrounds). The whole German media industry will closely watch the site when it goes live in October. Expectations are high. However, their willingness to start something new and fresh is, I think, what counts.

Despite the economic situation, I refuse to believe that journalism is dying or that I won't find a job. It is up to us – young journalists – to change the situation and to

experiment. I know, from projects that I have engaged with during my studies, that there is a certain atmosphere when working in a start-up, such as that group dynamic when everyone is pulling in the same direction. I am very optimistic that I will work as a journalist in the upcoming years. Who knows what this kind of work will look like, but I am sure it will be interesting. ☒

© Katharina Frick
www.indexoncensorship.org

**Katharina Frick**, 27, is currently pursuing a MA in journalism, media and globalisation, while working as a freelancer for the German Press Agency (DPA). She also runs her own journalism project on sustainability issues www.sustainyourfuture.com

# "I see a difficult future – for journalists and readers"

43(3): 24/25 | DOI: 10.1177/0306422014550963

Faced with high unemployment in his homeland, Italian journalist **Luca Rovinalti** moved to Prague – but celebrity news has followed

**W**HEN DECATHLETE ROMAN Šebrle and model Gabriela Kratochvílová recently became news anchors on one of the main private television networks in the Czech Republic, it was nothing new to me. Having started my career in Italy, I was very used to this celebrity-led, tabloid-style approach to journalism – an approach that appears to be growing across Europe.

When I worked for major private television channels in Italy in the 2000s, it was a time when journalism was turning into a space for gossip and stories were designed to trigger the audience's emotions. I remember days spent on the beach in Rimini, interviewing people on the perfect techniques for suntanning and asking girls about their preparations for the swimsuit season.

In 2010, I moved to the Czech Republic to do a one-year law programme at Charles University and decided to stay as they were cutting so many jobs at home. I have Polish roots, so I feel quite comfortable in eastern Europe and I am picking up the language. I am still freelancing for companies in Italy, but I am interested in working for English-language publications here and abroad.

In my career so far, I have already had some varied experiences – moving from Emilia-Romagna, in north-central Italy, to Milan and, in early 2010, to the Czech Republic, where I now run the International Press Club of Prague. This helped build my idea of a multicultural journalism, without national barriers and respecting cultural differences. I really hope this concept grows as the world becomes more globalised, with more local publications in different languages and international colleagues working together.

I co-founded the Prague Press Club in 2013 because I felt networking opportunities could be improved here and the existing institutions were not active enough. But I don't believe you need just a piece of paper, or a press card to be a journalist, as you do in Italy. I had to work for two years before I was able to get membership to the Italian journalists' association.

Italy's levels of unemployment – currently at 13 per cent, or 43 per cent for the under 25s – is having a big impact on journalism. It also means a lot of people are seeking work abroad. Mario Giordano, editor-in-chief of TG4, one of the main news programmes

of the Mediaset network in Italy, gave me this advice: "Journalism needs to change its mindset, not just its techniques. Those that know how to make this change are surviving. Bear in mind that the basic principles of journalism remain the same, whether you are using a carrier pigeon or a tweet."

I completely agree. Italian journalism has become an obstacle course that requires journalists to be up-to-date and adaptable to new technologies, in a market where there is almost no space for young talent. Many jobs are being outsourced or commissioned for a tiny freelance fee.

In my first job in a television newsroom, I was reluctant to move from work of "pure" journalism, to one that would include also the knowledge of filming techniques, technical equipment, video editing and broadcasting. But now I see that being a sort of one-man band is crucial in today's market.

In a society where bloggers and citizen journalists are gaining importance day by day, it is pointless to ignore innovation. It is essential to understand new technologies and use them properly, in the hope that readers are able to discern what is fact and what is exaggerated, what is reliable and what is not.

We are being increasingly bombarded by millions of sources of information, with real news mixed with the falsities, with advertising that camouflages as information and the pay-per-click philosophy that makes the first three words of an article its core. I see the future as a difficult place to be; both for readers, who need to discern between what is news and

## Now I see that being a sort of one-man band is crucial in today's market

what is not, and for journalists, who must juggle increasing competition, coming not only from professional colleagues but even by people who come to it from other professions, including models and athletes. ▣

© Luca Rovinalti
www.indexoncensorship.org

**Luca Rovinalti**, 27, is an Italian freelance journalist, based in Prague, the Czech Republic

ABOVE: Journalists work on their laptops during a press conference for Instagram in New York

# "Data journalism is the new frontier"

43(3): 26/27 | DOI: 10.1177/0306422014550963

**Athandiwe Saba** believes there is a strong future for investigative reporting – if only she can wrestle public information from the hands of government officials

**M**Y PASSION FOR journalism is based on the right that everyone should have access to information, based on section 36 of the South African constitution: "Everyone has the right of access to any information held by the state; and any information that is held by another person and that is required for the exercise or protection of any rights."

But today in our young democracy, that right is simply ignored, patronised, belittled

> **Freedom of information was written into the constitution in reaction to apartheid censorship, yet it remains constantly under threat**

or taken for granted by government officials and society as a whole. As a journalist for the Sunday newspaper City Press, I often have problems requesting information or comment from government agencies. My most recent struggle involved a simple request for the records of all schools in the country currently on the school nutrition plan. I have found myself resorting to quot-

ing legal rights and reminding officials that the information belongs to the people. Many months on, I am still waiting.

Our democratic government wrote freedom of information into the constitution in reaction to apartheid censorship, yet it remains constantly under threat. The Protection of State Information Bill, known as the "secrecy bill", has also been a point of contention since 2010. The aim was to regulate state information, weighing state interests against transparency and freedom of expression, but it would have surely restricted journalists, and proposed jail terms for reporters and whistleblowers that revealed classified information. It was approved by parliament in 2013, but has still not yet passed into law.

My biggest concern for the future is that if journalists struggle this much for information, what does that mean for the rest of the citizens in this country? If departments refuse access to school records, how would a parent be able to request the same information to uphold their child's rights?

It is worrying when politicians and authorities make irrational statements, such as asking the public to boycott publications: the ruling ANC party and its Youth League in the past two years have tried to censor the City Press and the Mail & Guardian newspapers separately over published material they felt offended the president or the party. There has also been talk, by the head of our state broadcaster, of licensing and controlling journalists.

My passion for data journalism – or computer-assisted journalism – became even stronger after attending a conference on the subject in the US city of Baltimore. It has enabled me think more critically about the numbers that government and non-governmental agencies bandy about. The idea hasn't taken a strong hold yet in newsrooms across South Africa, because it is seen as too time consuming and there have been too many job cuts. But there is a glimmer of hope. One of my editors referred to it as our "new frontier" and, in the past couple of months, I have been given more support to pursue data-driven stories in my newsroom.

I remember one of the facilitators at the US conference telling me I was lucky to come from a country where computer-assisted reporting has not really taken off yet. I was baffled. Then I realised he was referring to the fact that there is all that untapped information out there, mounds of records just waiting for me to use the skills I had learned. ▣

© Athandiwe Saba
www.indexoncensorship.org

**Athandiwe Saba,** 26, is an investigative, data journalist with City Press, a South African Sunday newspaper

LEFT: Protesters take part in a demonstration against the Protection of Information Bill in Cape Town on September 17, 2011

Credit: Sumaya Hisham/Reuters

# "How does a young, ethical journalist survive?"

43(3): 28/29 | DOI: 10.1177/0306422014550963

**Bhanuj Kappal** worries about editorial integrity in India being eroded by media owners and the pressures put on journalists to toe the line

INCREASINGLY, JOURNALISTS IN India are feeling isolated and under attack – from political leaders and the government, from the hordes of partisan internet trolls on comment threads and social media, and even from their own employers.

CNN-IBN's deputy editor, Sagarika Ghose, allegedly received instructions from

> ## Journalism is being dragged through the mud by a generation that has already made its name and its retirement money

the management at its parent company Network 18, not to post disparaging tweets about India's now prime minister, Narendra Modi, according to news website Scroll. in. Ghose refused to confirm or deny this to the Scroll.in reporter, but she did say that she saw a disturbing new trend where partisanship is celebrated while "journalists

who believe the politician is their natural adversary and systematically question all politicians, are seen as biased". She later quit.

This paints a pretty disturbing picture for young journalists like me, one in which the notion of editorial independence and integrity is fast being dismantled by media owners and management. And that's not counting the unpublished stories of editorial compromises and unethical practices that are a part of the conversation every time young journalists get together for a drink.

One of my former classmates from journalism school is so disillusioned by his experience at a popular English-language news channel in India that he's decided to quit broadcast journalism and work in the print media instead.

"They'd rather carry a visuals-based story over a public-interest story," he told me. Another, who worked at a prominent print magazine, has decided to give up journalism altogether and return to academia. As recently sacked political editor Hartosh Singh Bal of Open Magazine pointed out in an editorial: "Journalists entering the profession today have to make their compromises

with ownership and management at a much earlier stage of their career because they have been largely deprived of the protective shield of a good editor."

All of this leaves young journalists with a dilemma. Do you stay in an organisation where editorial independence is compromised? With jobs drying up and the scarcity of credible media organisations, how does a young journalist survive while staying committed to independent, ethical journalism? More importantly, what happens to the ideal of free and critical journalism when young journalists are being taught through public examples that the fiery, uncompromising journalist quickly becomes an unemployed one?

These are important questions for the future of journalism in a country where the media is becoming one of the big bogeymen in public discourse. Young journalists can do little more than watch despondently as their profession, and their future, is dragged through the mud by a generation that has already made its name and its retirement money. Combine this with the technological and economic challenges journalism is already facing globally – "streamification", "churnalism", the reduction of cultural journalism to "content" and "listicles" – and suddenly I find it hard to judge my friend for choosing the relative safety of an academic career. The future is bleak.

But young journalists aren't entirely helpless. Many of us have responded by taking up freelancing, foregoing economic security for freedom to choose our own stories and stay true to our ethics. Others choose to work in niche, but independent, news organisations. We're forming informal networks of support and information sharing, both online and in real life, with the idea that getting a story out to the public is more important than getting a byline or the credit for breaking it.

And for every Buzzfeed clone, the internet is throwing up spaces where issues ignored by the mainstream media get the attention and analysis they deserve. Websites like Scroll.in and Yahoo! Originals are giving young freelance journalists the opportunity to do the sort of original, independent journalism that traditional media no longer cares for. It's all nascent and imperfect, but it is the only hope we have for an Indian journalism that isn't completely beholden to corporate and political interests. ☒

© Bhanuj Kappal
www.indexoncensorship.org

**Bhanuj Kappal**, 26, is a Mumbai-based freelance journalist, who contributes to a number of publications including the Sunday Guardian, Yahoo! India and GQ India. He has a MA in international journalism from the School of Journalism, Media and Culture Studies at Cardiff University

# Attack on ambition

43(3): 30/33 | DOI: 10.1177/0306422014548397

Young journalists in Honduras are entering a profession where fear and corruption are the driving forces. Investigative reporter and human rights campaigner **Dina Meza** reports on how a ground-down generation is struggling to find its voice

**W**HEN THE JOURNALIST-OF-THE-YEAR awards were handed out in Honduras earlier this year, Cesario Padilla, a 21-year-old journalism student from the capital, Tegucigalpa, was unimpressed. "These are awarded by the powerful elite of politicians to quell their own consciences. I would never accept one," he said. Padilla is just starting out in his career, graduating next November, but he has set his sights on following a different path, away from the typical role models of glamorous and well-paid TV presenters. Padilla wants a career as an investigative reporter, but he is one of the few willing to take the risks involved.

Perhaps understandably, many young Honduran journalists don't want to put themselves in danger. At current estimates by the National Commission of Human Rights, 40 journalists have been killed since the 2009 military coup, when the army ousted President Manuel Zelaya. Many young people are instead turning to celebrity journalism or gossip columns rather than seeking to engage with social issues or take on tough assignments.

When I was a student in mid-1980s and early 1990s, there was more optimism. I studied journalism and law together, and felt that you could do a lot of good in Honduras through journalism. Some of my contemporaries felt the same and also wanted to make a difference by covering the big issues. But after the coup, many of the most motivated and critical journalists were forced into hiding. The military shut down several TV stations, radio stations and newspapers. There was a climate of fear, fuelled by deaths and disappearances of those who disagreed with the military's actions or demonstrated in favour of the ousted president. Later, when journalists returned to work, many chose to self-censor their work and keep a low profile. Some publications switched their whole editorial line.

Self-censorship has become a big problem in Honduras, and also a means for self-preservation. Many students have told me they wouldn't touch certain issues because they fear the consequences. As a very vocal reporter on human rights issues, I have been threatened repeatedly, forced to move house and temporarily left the country. Recently, I have had suspicious characters following me, photographers taking pictures of members of my family and phone calls at home at night from someone threatening to beat me up if I "continue to mess around". This happened just minutes after I posted a story on Facebook relating to the murder of a political activist.

I have also spoken to a lot of young journalists who feel that even if they wanted to

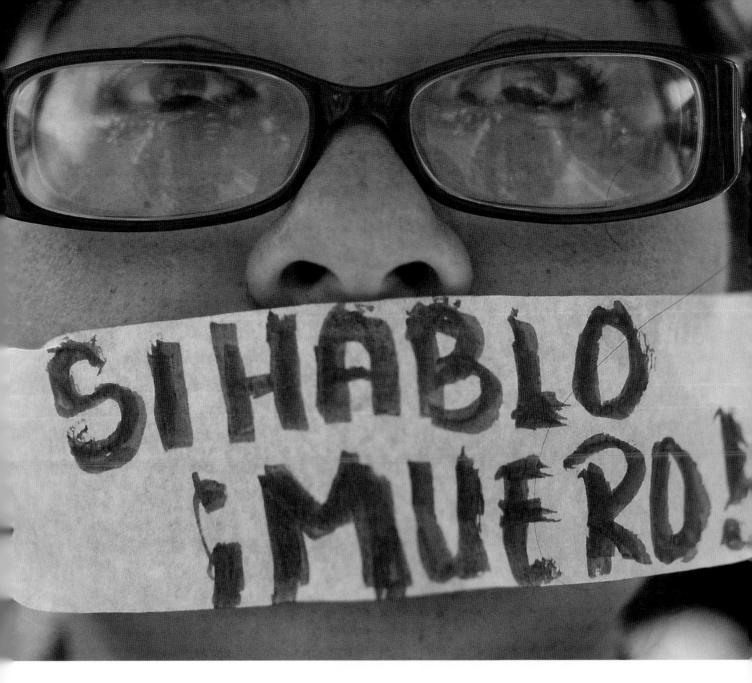

ABOVE: "I speak, I die" – a journalism student marching to demand an end to violence against the press, in Tegucigalpa, Honduras

make a difference, they'd have no outlets willing to publish them. When giving a talk on journalism, I remember once being approached by a student who said his self-esteem had been entirely worn down after a tutor told him he would have to bow to the will of media owners, instead of being able to challenge authority and write about he wanted. It was only when I explained how powerful media groups were not the only outlets and we could express ourselves by starting our own projects or working with existing online alternatives that he was encouraged. Soon afterwards, he told me

he found renewed enthusiasm and was no longer considering quitting journalism.

## Many stories go unreported in Honduras. Journalists are seen off with threats or bought with bribes

If universities produce submissive journalists, it is certain beneficial to media owners. The biggest media companies have wealthy owners with multiple business →

→ interests – land ownership, the arms industry, fast food industry, medicine – many of which become off-limits for reporters. A young journalist might write a good, balanced story – maybe on the indigenous community affected by a hydroelectric plant – where they'd interview all sides. Yet the publication won't publish it. I remember those days and how frustrating it was. When

BELOW: Coffin of Honduran television journalist Herlyn Espinal, who was killed in July

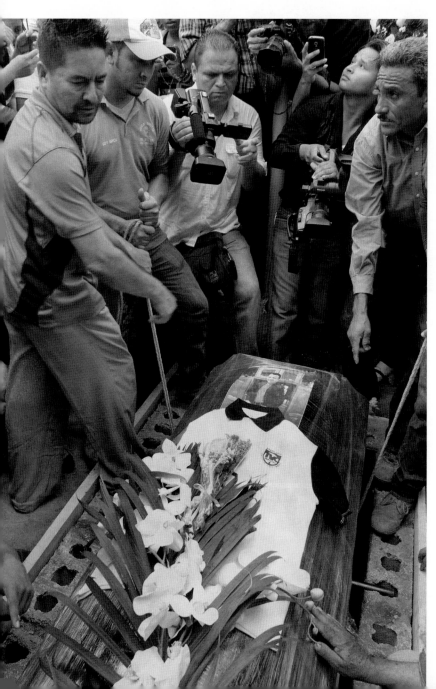

the first thing you do in the morning is see if your story has been published. Some never were.

Many stories go unreported in Honduras; journalists are seen off with threats or bought with bribes. Young journalists might find they are offered payment from an official who uses public money to pay them for a flattering profile. With wages so low, it is so easy to succumb to corruption. Many publications also have to be careful of criticising the government as the media is heavily reliant on money from state advertising.

The foreign media offer few opportunities for budding locals. Some of the big international agencies are present in Honduras, including AFP and Reuters, but their vacancies are few and far between. And although some – such as Mexican news agency Notimex – can be quite challenging sometimes in its reporting, many correspondents, while not being officially censored by their companies, self-censor to stay out of trouble.

But some young journalists are experimenting with alternatives: using their own blogs, Facebook, Twitter. The student website Frusps.com brings together young people from different faculties, not just the journalism school. But there is no university-supported student newspaper to offer the students the chance to practise their skills and write freely, without media owners on their backs.

The National Autonomous University of Honduras has recently reformed its school of journalism, now the school of communication sciences. Students can now do a post-graduate in social media or radio technology. A move with the times, perhaps, but it does nothing to strengthen the development of investigative journalism.

Journalism students at this university attend ethics classes three times a week, but some students complain that the course is disconnected from the rest of their studies. There is a sense that the principles are

say affects the interests of powerful groups." You'll lose your job, or worse.

Freedom of expression and freedom to information are vital rights, connecting to and underpinning all other rights. In a country when there is little freedom of expression, there will inevitably be violence. The next

# Students are taught to be honest in their reporting, while being reminded that they need to be submissive to keep their jobs

generation is now taking the reins to direct the future of our nation's journalism. They urgently need support. ☒

© Dina Meza
www.indexoncensorship.org

*Translation by Amanda Hopkinson*

presented as ideals, rather than practicalities that can be applied in the workplace. So, theoretically, they are taught to be balanced and honest in their reporting, while being reminded that the bottom line is that they need to be submissive to keep their jobs.

There are, of course, lecturers who are trying their best to motivate their students. One lecturer at the university, who requested to remain anonymous, says that more must be done to strengthen the social function of journalists: "Students today want to study journalism in order to appear on television or on radio, and are inclined to go for gossip and celebrity stuff, rather than journalism rooted in serious research."

Investigative and news-orientated journalists in Honduras come under constant pressure. The elite wield the power, and much of the truth of what is going on in the country remains concealed. Haidy Carrasco, a 20-year-old journalism student, says: "Freedom of speech doesn't exist if what you

**Dina Meza** is a leading human rights journalist in Honduras. She was a nominee in the journalism category of Index on Censorship's 2014 Freedom of Expression awards. She is currently working on a project, Periodismo y Democracia (Journalism and Democracy), to establish a network of university students in Honduras to offer training on reporting controversial topics, and how to use technology and media tools to protect themselves. It also intends to build a heightened awareness of human rights and journalism as a means of social engagement. The project will include a website focusing on freedom of expression

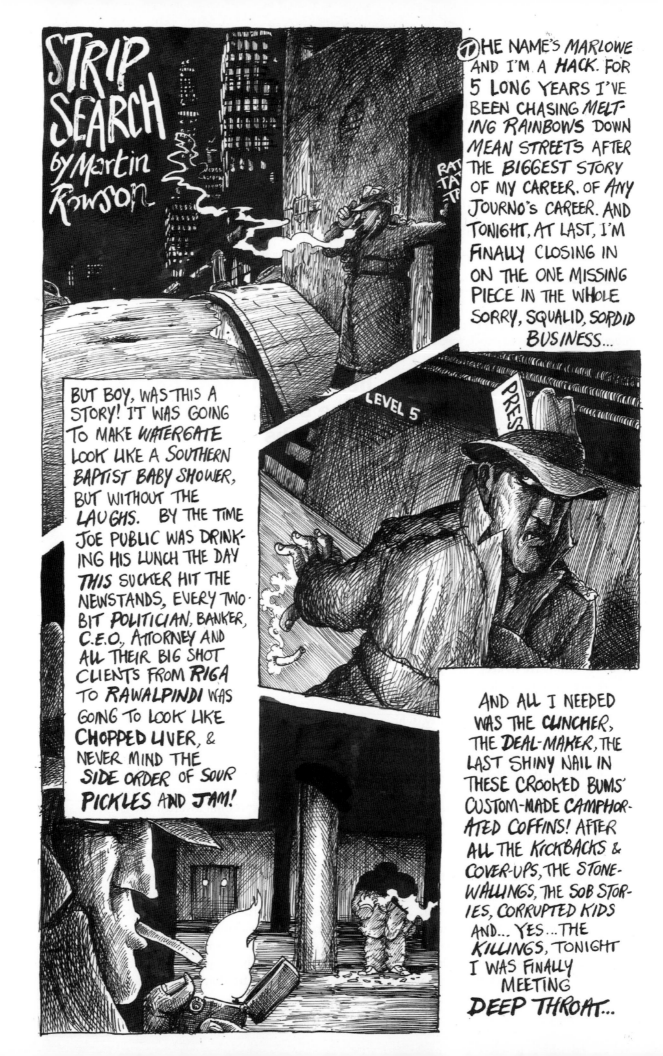

# Generation why

43(3): 36/38 | DOI: 10.1177/0306422014547671

Will the next generation of journalists work with the public to hold the powerful to account, asks **Ian Hargreaves**

**THE ANXIETY THAT** journalism is dying, dead or disabled is anything but new. A hundred years ago, newspapers said radio broadcasting would destroy them, with the result that in the 1920s the fledgling BBC was banned from broadcasting news before 7pm. It was rather like taxi drivers taking strike action against a cab-hailing app today.

Twenty years ago, US shareholder capitalism, with its emphasis upon advertising revenues and quarterly profits reports, was powerfully argued to be compromising journalism's public mission.

In the last decade-and-a-half, however, these and other earlier crises have been shaken into relief by what has been the news business's most genuinely difficult decade in a century with newspaper readership declining dramatically in most countries.

One reason all this turbulence should provoke cautious optimism rather than despair about journalism's future is that we have now started to experience the new forms of journalism to which the internet is giving birth, enabling us to understand better what has been variously called "the fifth estate" and the "networked public sphere".

The components of this new ecology, from Twitter microblogs to data journalism, are numerous, diverse and shifting. Philanthropists have stepped in to fund some investigative journalism. Crowdfunding has helped reporters take on overseas assignments.

Whatever view you take about the complexities of the Wikileaks/Chelsea Manning/Edward Snowden chain of events, we have seen how individuals, upstart organisations and whistleblowers, none of them professional journalists, can collaborate with the media to challenge holders of power.

We have also seen how hyper-local journalism, some it from "citizen journalists", has re-shaped news and discussion, and how street-level activism of the kind represented by the Occupy movement has both challenged and contributed to the emerging ecology of global news and comment. Look at the way that the political activism represented by Avaaz or Moveon now intersects with the emergence of cause-based, viral journalism of the kind practised by the likes of Upworthy.com. Or read the memorandum to staff circulated by Jonah Peretti, founder of Buzzfeed, in which he refers to David Halberstam's 1979 book The Powers That Be. Likening Buzzfeed to the emergence of Time magazine in its ability to attract new audiences with a fresh approach to news presentation, Peretti is building a global network of reporters and editors. As Harvard legal scholar Yochai Benkler has argued: this "networked public sphere" enables players "to some extent complement and to some extent compete with each other". For Benkler, predecessor models are the open-source software movement and Wikipedia.

ABOVE: Buzzfeed's New York newsroom – the site has moved into foreign news coverage as well as humorous lists

If you share this sense of guarded optimism about the emergence of a fifth estate, the online-era news, comment and information environment of which the bruised and battered fourth estate is a non-dominant component, then the most relevant question ceases to concern national regulatory regimes for newspapers. Rather, we need to ask: what decisions do we need to take to ensure that the fifth estate does an even better job than its predecessor in holding the powerful to account?

Our primary focus can only be the internet because the way that it works or is inhibited from working will determine more than anything else the extent to which journalism, in its new, broader, more flexible fifth estate definition, will succeed in serving the public interest, taking advantage of "open access" regimes and big data analytics.

For this fifth estate to thrive, the core priority is freedom of expression for everyone, not only journalists. It follows that even very important other rights, like privacy and data protection, should be subordinate.

The most complex single issue is the conundrum concerning the governance of the internet, which is currently on the agenda of dozens of international institutions but the responsibility of none. Meanwhile, many countries increasingly constrain the way the internet works within their own boundaries. China's great firewall, along with other more vicious forms of restraint, offers a model much envied among the non-democratically minded. It regulates the internet on a

## Europe often sounds like a wounded beast, lashing out at the super-species of Google, Facebook, Amazon and Apple

national basis without apparently disabling the technology's ability to drive e-commerce. The price is less access to information for the public when these governments don't want their citizens to know what's going on.

For Europe, these challenges are the source of much agony. Whether debating the European Union's apparently unattainable "digital single market" (needed to bring the pro-trade principles of the Common →

→ Market to the online world), copyright, data protection or privacy, Europe too often sounds like a wounded beast, lashing out at the dominant and alien super-species of Google, Facebook, Amazon, Apple and the rest.

In the absence of any serious European competitors to these general, and global, internet platforms, the risk is that Europe's manner slides from anxious to protective and then to protectionist, leading to less rather than more innovation and a further downward twist in Europe's productivity crisis, along with worrying restrictions on the public's right to know. It is in this vein that Germany has tried to extend copyright in news to impede the work of news aggregators. The same climate of opinion encourages the European Court of Justice to support the "right to be forgotten" so that somebody somewhere (currently and absurdly, Google) must decide to whom this right is available. Meanwhile, on the edge of Europe, the Turkish authorities think they can close down Twitter and in the countries of the Arab Spring journalists are again being thrown into jail simply for doing their jobs. To the east, President Vladimir Putin, having re-annexed broadcasting to the Kremlin, ponders his options with regard to an internet, which is the closest thing Russia has to a site of free-ish speech.

The US courts, meanwhile, continue to churn their way through cases concerning intellectual property rights, the licensing of broadcasters and the behaviour of internet service providers which also contribute to re-shaping the landscape in which US journalism takes place. These decisions frequently and pivotally return to the First Amendment to the constitution, which says that Congress shall do nothing to abridge the right of Americans to a free press and so to free expression. A good example of such a case is the long-running and still incomplete Google Books case, which sets the technology giant against authors and publishers.

There are signs, however, that "old" media are finding ways to navigate the new world. If the BBC is doing its job – and the figures for usage of and trust in its broadcast and online news services suggest that mostly it is – public alarm about loss of journalistic heft among UK newspaper companies is mitigated. According to Ofcom's latest research on news in the UK, 53 per cent said the BBC was their most important source of news.

We also now have clear signs that some news organisations with their roots in print are making their way to sustainable positions in the online world. Although Paul Dacre, the Daily Mail's pugnacious editor, famously said as recently as 1999 that this was "bullshit dot com", Mail Online is now the most visited newspaper-owned news website in the world.

Every student of journalism knows that Thomas Jefferson once said that given a choice between a government without newspapers or newspapers without government, he would not hesitate to choose the latter. In a world in which newspapers and those who own them no longer dominate the fifth estate as they did the fourth, Jefferson's argument today applies directly and persuasively to the internet. This requires us to ask ourselves urgently and consistently: how free do we want the internet to be? How hard are we prepared to press for this and through what institutional mechanisms? What trade-offs are we willing to accept? For the future of journalism and for the future of democracy, these now are the biggest questions. ⌧

© **Ian Hargreaves**
www.indexoncensorship.org

**Ian Hargreaves** is professor of digital economy at Cardiff University and author of Digital Opportunity: A review of Intellectual Property and Growth for the UK Government. His book: Journalism – a Very Short Introduction has just been published in a revised edition by Oxford University Press

# Making waves

43(3): 39/41 | DOI: 10.1177/0306422014547479

Russian radio station Echo of Moscow is one of the last bastions of a free media not toeing Putin's line. **Helen Womack** meets its founder

**T**HE ANSWER IS always a firm "no" whenever the Kremlin tries to put pressure on Russian radio station Echo of Moscow to slant its news coverage. "It's no, and that's that," says Sergei Buntman, co-founder of the radio station that is often described as the last bastion of free media in the country.

"There are attempts to influence us, hints that we should 'put that on' or 'take that off'," he says. "We may sack a journalist ourselves but if the suggestion comes from outside, never! I've heard Alexei Venediktov, the editor, say, 'I'd sack that fellow but Vyacheslav Volodin [of the presidential administration] wants me to so I can't.' It's a matter of principle."

Buntman receives me in his book-lined office. On the door is a street sign reading "Old Trafford: Sir Matt Busby Way", a nod to the Manchester United manager who was his childhood hero. "Can I break the law?" he asks, as he lights up his pipe in violation of Russia's new anti-smoking rules.

I'm seeing Buntman rather than Venediktov because Echo has said its famous, crazy-haired editor-in-chief doesn't meet the foreign press. Asked why, the mustachioed French-speaking Buntman says it's nothing sinister, just a "division of labour". Buntman, who started out as an announcer on Soviet radio, co-founded Echo together with its first editor Sergei Korzun in 1990.

These men are not dissidents, just journalists dedicated to professional principles of objectivity and balance. But in President Vladimir Putin's Russia, where almost all the media spout state propaganda, that position looks like radical nonconformity, and it seems a wonder that Echo survives.

There are various theories as to how Echo gets away with it. Some say the radio and associated website, with a following of nearly one million in Moscow and three million in the regions, is tolerated because it allows the intelligentsia to let off steam, with little impact on the rest of the TV-watching country. Others say it allows the Kremlin to argue to the world that free speech is not dead in Russia. And one theory has it that Kremlin staff themselves depend on Echo to be properly informed because they can't rely on their own propaganda.

Buntman has another explanation. "It's no miracle and no wonder," he says. "You'd be surprised but a lot actually depends on us. Many journalists just give in too soon; they give up at the first hurdle."

Does he mean they engage in self-censorship? "No, they take up a political position; they do this themselves. It's professional suicide, of course. You can't present yourself as a journalist and then do propaganda. There *is* pressure but to get killed as a journalist, you've really got to earn that. Not everyone is granted the fate of a Politkovskaya."

The journalist Anna Politkovskaya was shot dead in the stairwell of the block of flats where she lived on 7 October 2006. She →

ABOVE: Editor-in-chief of Echo of Moscow, Alexei Venediktov, speaks with Putin during the 2012 Russian Print Media Awards ceremony

→ investigated killings and disappearances in Chechnya for the newspaper Novaya Gazeta, the most robust of the Russian print

## One theory is that Kremlin staff depend on Echo for information because they can't rely on their own propaganda

media. There is also the opposition-friendly internet TV channel Dozhd (Rain), which gave a platform to two feminists from Pussy Riot on their release from jail. But all the major TV channels, from which the majority of Russians get their news, promote the president's policies and views.

It was not always thus. The decade of Boris Yeltsin's rule may have been difficult and turbulent, but the free media flourished and Russia produced some very fine journalism. In the 1990s, NTV stood out for its inquiring spirit, which makes it all the sadder that the channel now specialises in hatchet-job "documentaries" about Kremlin critics. Some former NTV journalists have found asylum at Echo, in which Gazprom Media holds a 66 per cent stake and journalists 34 per cent.

According to Buntman, a generation of Russian journalists has been virtually lost, so the station hires young reporters and trains them to the highest standards.

"A reporter never invents and never conceals," he says. "In the 1990s, we drew up a charter of journalists' ethics – you can't be a journalist and a party member, you can't have a conflict of interest, all that sort of thing. And everyone at Echo signs this charter when they sign a contract to work for us."

Balance, balance and again balance is the Echo mantra. Buntman remembers that in 1991, the year of the hardline coup against Mikhail Gorbachev, the editors were upset because they couldn't get a comment from the GKChP, the junta that briefly seized power, to balance all the views coming from the democratic side." We invite everyone to speak on Echo," he says. "We invite Sergei Markov [a pro-Kremlin political analyst]. We know he'll talk rubbish. Let him talk rubbish; I won't moderate him."

During the crisis over Ukraine, Echo has ruffled feathers both in Moscow and Kiev by airing the full gamut of opinions and refusing to take sides. Its reporting of the tragic fire in Odessa on 2 May, when over 40 people, mainly pro-Russian activists, were burnt to death inside the city's trade union building, stood out in contrast to the tendentious coverage of Russian and Ukrainian media. It appears both sides threw Molotov cocktails and how exactly the fire started is still to be established.

"We were suspicious that the fire was hardly over before one side was blaming 'Russian provocateurs' and the other was pointing the finger at Pravy Sektor (a Ukrainian nationalist group)," says Buntman. " There was a fire; that was a fact. We dispatched three reporters to try to piece together, millimetre by millimetre, what happened. We still only have preliminary conclusions."

Likewise, Buntman says, only international criminal experts will be able to apportion blame in the deaths of some 100 people, killed by snipers in Maidan (Independence Square), Kiev, in February.

And what about the 1999 apartment block bombings in Moscow? "Yes," says Buntman, "questions, questions, questions. Journalists should have questions, not premature answers."

Covering Ukraine, Echo is careful in its choice of language, says Buntman. "Do we call the pro-Russians 'separatists'? Yes, because they want to break away. 'Militias?' Yes, because they are irregular armed forces. Those terms are not coloured either way. But for the word 'terrorist' to be used, there must be a real act of terror."

While Echo spoke of the "interim government" that replaced ousted Ukranian president Viktor Yanukovych, most Russian media called it a "fascist junta". Now that Petro Poroshenko has been elected president in Kiev and is talking to Putin, those media are having to row back on the junta label.

"I don't envy the propagandists," says Buntman. "They have to think up new lies every day. Our life is much easier." I ask whether Venediktov – for it is the editor-in-chief who has the job of drinking whisky with Kremlin officials and even meeting Putin himself – has had any contact with the Kremlin leader over the Ukraine crisis.

"No," says Buntman. "Lately we've had the feeling that we can't talk to him. One official said to us that he had jumped from a high building and thought he was flying.

The only reason he still thought he was flying was because the building was very high."

But Venediktov has met Putin on numerous occasions in the past and the relationship is clear. "From the start," says Buntman, "Alexei took the right position. Putin sees the world simply, in terms of friends, enemies and traitors. We can't be traitors because we were never friends in the first place. Echo is an enemy."

# I don't envy the propagandists. They have to think up new lies every day. Our life is easier

Putin himself said this? "Oh yes, quite clearly, 14 years ago, at the time NTV was destroyed."

And if Putin has any suspicion that Echo is secretly financed by the CIA, all he has to do is look at the station's rather shabby offices and low salaries, says Buntman, with a twinkle in his eye. ☒

© Helen Womack
www.indexoncensorship.org

**Helen Womack** has reported from Moscow since 1985. She currently works in Russia for The Sydney Morning Herald. Her book The Ice Walk: Surviving the Soviet Break-Up and the New Russia is published by Melrose Books

# Switched on and off

43(3): 42/45 | DOI: 10.1177/0306422014549149

News investigations and curating user-generated content are upcoming trends at TV stations. **Debora Halpern Wenger** reports on the challenges ahead in bringing the public news it can trust

**M**OST AMERICANS STILL get their news from television. Over the course of a month, more than 70 per cent of US adults watch local TV news and 65 per cent watch the networks. On a global level, an even greater percentage of news consumers say they often rely on television as a news source. Eighty-five per cent of those in Denmark, 79 per cent in the UK and 75 per cent of Brazilians say they access TV news on a weekly basis.

But with an explosion of digital options and a myriad of viewing devices, the question for broadcasters is: "How do we bring the public information it doesn't already know?" Stations in the US appear to be looking at putting more resources into news investigations and in fact checking viewer submitted reports. If legacy news organisations don't adapt and hold on too tightly to the way things used to be, they risk letting nostalgia put them out of business.

Data suggests that the audience for television news is "greying". Today, only a third of Americans aged 18-29 say they regularly watch television news programmes. Globally, only those age 45 and older consider television their main news source. Traditional broadcasters have to try to attract younger audiences – via online, mobile or new digital devices developed in the future – while also embracing the 24/7 news cycle and adapting to the decline of appointment viewing.

Shrinking TV news audiences since the 1990s heyday have hit advertising revenues in the US. Add to this the economic downturn of 2008-2009 and the explosion of digital competitors chasing the same advertisers, and, for a while, the future looked grim. In 2008, the TV news workforce in the US was reduced by 4.3 per cent, with another decrease of 1.5 per cent in 2009. Since then, however, things have improved. By 2013, staffing levels were just a little below a record high seen in 2000.

Part of the reason for the improvement is the expansion of revenue streams. Television stations in the US now make a significant amount of money from cable companies paying retransmission fees. By using data compression techniques, a TV station can use its single TV signal to broadcast more than one programme simultaneously, a practice known as multicasting.

This changing business model, which still includes traditional advertising revenue, ensures the survival of television news in the near term. But TV news organisations cannot fully inoculate themselves from losses to digital competitors. If they want to retain a significant role in satisfying the public's right to know, they have to rethink their content and delivery methods, too.

Despite the proliferation of sensationalised stories and shows stacked with celebrity news, smart TV managers understand that serious

ABOVE: HBO series The Newsroom attempts to capture life at a modern TV news channel

Credit: HBO/Everett/Rex

local coverage will help keep the best TV stations in business well into the future. Understanding the importance of strong journalism, some local television stations have recently ramped up or recommitted themselves to producing more watchdog and investigative journalism. The executive director of the US-based Investigative Reporters and Editors (IRE) organisation says that its 2014 conference hosted one of the largest contingents of broadcast journalists ever. Gannett, one of the biggest TV news companies in the US, sent 150 journalists to the event.

Recent investigative "wins" for local television stations in the US include a station in Houston, Texas uncovering evidence of widespread food stamp fraud, a station in Los Angeles that exposing a lax regulatory regime that led to tour bus accidents and a

## Only a third of Americans aged 18-29 regularly watch television news programmes

40-part investigation by a station in New Orleans that revealed how a local coroner had wasted millions of tax dollars – a story that ended with him pleading guilty in federal court. All of these stories helped →

→ protect the interests of local citizens and helped make local audiences better informed.

But it would be naive to think quality content alone can keep television news organisations in business. The power shift from news producers to news consumers is now permanent. No longer is the top-down "we decide what news is" approach going to work. The audience is now generating and distributing video news content itself, and television news organisations must take on a new role of curator to help viewers sift through and understand the mountains of information available to them.

One of the best-known examples of a television news organisation that has institutionalised this user-generated content is

## The ability to crowdscource the news has the potential to make the public better informed

CNN's iReport. The initiative was launched in 2006 as a way to allow people from all around the world to contribute pictures and video of breaking news stories. According to the website, the unit's producers handle submissions from 750,000 registered members, which translates into an average of 500 iReports a day. A fraction of those are vetted and approved for CNN's newscasts or other digital platforms, but CNN has recognised that reporting the news is now much more about two-way communication. Listening is key; not only will audiences tell you what kinds of stories they do and don't like, but they also often have their own stories or specialised information to share, which can add an entirely new layer to news coverage.

Local TV news operations are also routinely using user-generated content during breaking news situations and for special event coverage. This ability to crowdsource the news has the potential to make the public better informed.

The fact that technological developments have prompted more people to take an active role in creating and sharing news – including video – will help sustain the medium for years to come. Television is a form of journalism that continues to wield great power, generate great profits and command massive audiences. If redefined to include video news in general, those audiences become even larger and more significant.

On the other hand, there are plenty of chances for TV news to make a mess of things. Those who lead newsrooms can turn away from relevant and important news coverage and risk long-term survival for short-term audience gains. They can ignore the power of the audience and forgo the opportunity to add new voices to their coverage. And they can become too narrowly focused on distributing their journalism through a big box in the living room. However, the smart bet says they won't. ☒

© Debora Halpern Wenger
www.indexoncensorship.org

**Debora Halpern Wenger** worked as assistant news director at WFLA-TV in Florida, USA, before joining the University of Mississippi as an associate professor. She conducts multimedia training sessions for journalists in newsrooms around the USA. She is co-author of the book Advancing the Story: Journalism in a Multimedia World. She tweets @dhwenger

# "Local TV news will reinvent itself – again"

........................................

**Taylor Walker** *speaks to veteran TV news reporter and director Gerry Wardwell about how the industry is changing*

In the mid-1990s, Gerry Wardwell remembers laughing with fellow TV news journalists at actress Michelle Pfeiffer, playing a broadcaster effortlessly filming live shots in front of a prison riot. Pfeiffer's character in Up Close & Personal clearly didn't have to worry about hooking up countless cables to a news truck. "It was like magic," he says. "But now that is a reality." Today, everything is immediate.

Wardwell's career spans over 10 stations and almost 30 years. He has produced broadcasts, created morning shows, and currently serves as assistant news director at WCVB-TV Channel 5 in Massachusetts. During this time, the industry has transformed by new technology.

# The challenge is how do you make news compelling if everyone already knows it?

"Today's newsrooms are heavily digital, with journalists glued to devices," says Wardwell. "Technology just keeps getting better. Local TV news has changed so much in the past 30 years, but I think it will reinvent itself again." As the web creates more consumer choice and more personalisation, he believes local TV stations will increasingly become the verifier, confirming or denying things people have read online.

In his earlier years, smaller news services were practically married to wire services, staff used typewriters, and nothing was immediate. The reporter would often drive hundreds of miles for a story and then hundreds of miles back to record it. Once, in the 1980s Wardwell's station in Georgia covered a funeral in Washington state and the station flew the report back to Georgia for transmission; now that footage is transmitted digitally. "That idea would give a news director a heart attack now," says Wardwell of the delay.

Social media has been the biggest change. "You can find out things now without a TV newsroom," he says. "The challenge is how do you make news interesting and compelling if everyone already know it?" For Wardwell, Twitter has become a wire service and a way to connect instantly with audiences. "As a journalist you're always thinking, how can I use this [social media] to drive people to this story, this broadcast," he says.

Wardwell still walks into the WCVB newsroom every day, loaded with new ideas. "I'm not shocked by any of the changes," he says. "It's just the news now never stops." X

© Taylor Walker
www.indexoncensorship.org

**Taylor Walker** is currently working as an intern at WCVB-TV in Boston, as well as studying broadcast journalism at Boston University. She tweets @taylorreports

# Right to reply

43(3): 46/50 | DOI: 10.1177/0306422014549295

The BBC tackles allegations of bias, stereotyping, bad taste in its weekly right-to-reply programme, Newswatch. As the show marks its 10th year, presenter **Samira Ahmed** assesses the criticism, and looks at why responding to viewers is important

**"WHAT'S THE POINT** of Newswatch-BBC when all you do is say the complainants are wrong and the BBC is perfect?" asked viewer Paul Farnhill in a recent tweet to our programme, encapsulating the most repeated criticism in the series' first decade. Newswatch was established in 2004 in response to the Hutton Inquiry, which investigated the death of government weapons' adviser David Kelly and strongly criticised the BBC's reporting. The purpose of the show was to make BBC News' decision-making more transparent and accountable.

Asking questions, via Twitter, by letter or in the studio, doesn't always guarantee the answers that viewers want, or even a "sorry", but Newswatch does have an impact on those in charge. Anecdotally we know that managers, editors, producers and reporters watch it, and are very aware of it being watched by their colleagues and bosses. Informally, some contact us with their own views and concerns.

Viewers who choose to watch a TV bulletin from a public-service broadcaster, rather than skimming the internet for popular clips, are seeking an authoritative take on what is important. This means they are quick to notice careless or partial coverage by journalists who are under deadline pressure or just being lazy. They also flag up stories editors might be consistently ignoring or misreporting.

"That's not news" is our second most frequent complaint. The rolling news coverage that followed the death of young celebrity Peaches Geldof in April, when airtime was filled with messages taken off Twitter, drew the ire of many viewers. One, Rob Izzy, wrote: "Yes, an announcement and biography with comments from her family. But her taxi driver? Were you that desperate to drag it out longer?" The BBC News channel controller Sam Taylor said the breaking story drew a huge TV audience and 13.5 million readers to the BBC website story, the highest number ever. But could the statistics also prove that this sort of heavily promoted coverage perpetuates a dumbed-down news environment?

Then there's the serious complaint of omission, or comparative under-reporting. Days of simultaneous rolling coverage across two TV channels after Nelson Mandela's death in December 2013 prompted 2,000 viewers to complain that vital information about damaging storms hitting the east coast of England was not provided. Were London-based news bosses too obsessed with their own carefully prepared tributes?

The very first Newswatch I presented in September 2012 involved quizzing the head

ABOVE: Samira Ahmed in the Newswatch studio

of editorial standards, David Jordan, about why Newsnight had dropped its sex abuse investigation into BBC presenter Jimmy Savile. The story was subsequently picked up by its rival commercial TV station, ITV, and led to a major criminal investigation, uncovering links between powerful figures in entertainment, politics and the police. The BBC's decision to drop, rather than park, the investigation was because bosses were concerned that journalists only had the testimony of alleged victims, "just the women", as Newsnight editor Peter Rippon wrote in an email to producer Meirion Jones. It does seem though as if the revelations have had

a major and overall positive impact on how news organisations, police and prosecutors have treated the testimony of complainants who have come forward since. The Crown

## Accusations of political bias often draw coordinated complaints

Prosecution Service based their subsequent, successful prosecution of broadcaster Stuart Hall on the testimony of a number of different women, each of whom had come forward separately with individual accounts  →

→ that proved a matching and consistent pattern of abuse.

Accusations of political bias often draw coordinated complaints. The BBC got more than 6,000 at the end of June after the corporation's TV news programmes failed to give more than a few seconds of airtime to footage of an estimated 5,000-strong demonstration against government's austerity cuts. The march had started outside the BBC's news headquarters in London.

## Broadcast news is only as good as the individuals making it. And viewers regularly catch out lazing, careless and stereotyped stories

The number of complaints was far greater than the 1,000 back in September 2013 that had been lodged over the BBC's cursory treatment of a pro-National Health Service (NHS) rally by 50,000 people on the eve of the Conservative Party Conference in Manchester.

In both cases BBC management declined to come on the programme, offering a written statement about why they felt the coverage was fair. Nonetheless, the complaints aired to more than a million viewers during the show's regular Saturday morning slot on BBC News. The central charge was that the corporation was effectively censoring dissenting voices and thereby providing a distorted picture of public opinion that was undemocratic.

The complaints about the NHS rally also highlighted a more complex view held by some people, that the BBC's coverage of Britain's health service is relentlessly negative and scandal-focused. They believe the BBC's reporting undermines the NHS and feeds the Conservative Party's political agenda by suggesting that services will only be improved if they are taken over by private companies.

Theories about alleged BBC bias have always flourished on all sides of the political spectrum, but it does seem that the main British broadcasters cover mass demonstrations with minimal frequency and detail unless there is violence. The rise of complex accreditation systems at many major political events can make it easy for reporters to stay within the secure cordons and obey the security guards telling them not to film.

Astute viewers are also quick to challenge careless language and lazy stereotyping. In January 2013, a number complained about BBC reporters describing the armed Islamists who attacked an Algerian gas installation and took the workers hostage, as "insurgents" or "militants". Why not "terrorists"? A BBC TV news report in June 2014, ahead of the Scotland referendum, canvassed women voters in an Edinburgh beauty parlour. Viewer Zofia Jordan asked: "How about choosing scientists, engineers, bank workers? BBC couldn't approach women in different careers, such as in science or teaching? We do a lot more than just making other women look pretty."

Taste and decency is where claims over freedom of expression are the most contentious. The murder of soldier Lee Rigby in May 2013 by two Islamist radicals was filmed by a passerby in south-east London. ITV bought the footage, showing one of the attackers with bloodied hands, explaining his motivation at length. The BBC's decision to run an extract on its evening bulletins shocked many viewers who felt it gave jihadists the publicity they craved. The head of the BBC Newsroom, Mary Hockaday, said the story required it. The carefully edited footage was preceded with "health" warnings and the limited showings were not gratuitous, but complainants remained sceptical. To them this was an example of newsmakers failing to act responsibly or in the best interests of their audience.

Most crucial of all is the question of how many viewers each formal complaint represents. Is one the equivalent of 1,000 viewers? Or could there be 10,000 who felt the same but sat shouting at the TV or turned off their tablet in annoyance? This is not voting and viewers aren't always right, but impartial broadcast news is an essential part of an informed democracy. Even with charters and a much stronger regulatory framework than written media, broadcast news is only as good as the individuals making it. And viewers regularly catch out lazy, careless and stereotyped stories.

Since Newswatch began, social media, notably Twitter, has played an increasing role in raising awareness of events that are not being covered, and has helped coordinate instant challenges to missing stories. The #BringBackOurGirls campaign, initiated in Nigeria after the kidnapping of 200 schoolgirls in April, spread worldwide. It didn't end Boko Haram's campaign of abduction, but it did bring international news coverage and political attention to a long-running crisis.

Licence-fee funded or not, every news organisation should acknowledge that listening to complaints is vital. Journalists need to be reminded about who they serve, and be kept alert to their duties of impartiality and truth. ☒

© Samira Ahmed
www.indexoncensorship.org

**Samira Ahmed** is a BBC journalist and the presenter of Newswatch

||||||||||||||||||||||||||||||||||||||||||||||||||||||||||||||||||||||||||||||||||||||||||||||||||||||||||||||||||

# Readers as editors

**Stephen Pritchard**, *past president of the Organization of News Ombudsmen, writes on the growing importance of news ombudsman and the call for more media transparency*

Gone are the days when newspapers could make announcements with Olympian detachment, sure in the knowledge that few would contradict them. Now, the world is full of internet-savvy fact-checkers who can challenge a story but who can also contribute vivid first-hand accounts or expert knowledge to enrich a newspaper's reporting.

Being open to your readers makes all sorts of sense, journalistically and commercially. It's all part of a movement away from the "tablets of stone" approach, which began some years ago with an honest recognition of the media's fallibility.

Step forward those doughty readers' editors, also known as public editors, toiling in media all around the world. They work within newsrooms, dealing with complaints, publishing corrections and writing columns on their organisation's journalism. They act independently of the editor, and represent the audience, not the organisation.

You'll find them at (to name just a few) The New York Times; The Hindu; The Star, Nairobi; Folha de São Paulo; SBS Australia; The Los Angeles Times; and The Guardian.

The principle behind news ombudsmanship is simple: news organisations hold governments and institutions to account, so they in turn should be accountable to their audiences.

Yes, most media have letters pages and comment threads, customer service departments and marketing focus groups, but how many have a staffer in the newsroom who stands back from the fray and really listens to them and, furthermore, acts on their comments from a truly independent position inside the organisation?

It's all about transparency. From transparency flows trust. Show your readers that you care about accuracy, about fairness, about getting the story right and you gain their trust. If they trust you, they will read you.

There is a strong business case for accountability. If the paper has broad enough shoulders to take some criticism, it can be a hugely beneficial appointment. It clears the editor's desk of nagging complaints, allowing him or her to get on with the job; it shows you actively care about accuracy; it promotes loyalty within your readership and it significantly reduces litigation costs.

I have recently finished my second term as president of the Organization of News Ombudsmen, the global umbrella group for readers' editors and broadcasting standards editors, during which time media in Germany, Cyprus, Portugal, Argentina, Albania and even Myanmar have appointed an advocate for their audiences. These are hopeful times for transparency.

And the job isn't standing still. As the media develops, so the news ombudsman must embrace Twitter and other forms of social media, plus blogging and the demands of 24-hour news cycles. And neither is it a fixed institution.

The government in Argentina has appointed Cynthia Ottaviano as its first "defender of the public" on matters involving broadcast media. The former TV and newspaper journalist travels the country holding public meetings and encouraging debate on the content of programmes. In her first year she tackled the portrayal of violence against women on television, watershed scheduling, better programmes for children and the withdrawal of cultural and educational cable channels.

While no one would pretend that everything in the garden is rosy and Argentina's president, Cristina Fernández de Kirchner, has been accused of trying to curb the critical press by cutting state advertising contracts and breaking up the biggest opposition media group, it's still a big step forward from 30 years ago, when Argentina's media were regulated by a committee made up entirely of officers from the armed forces, with no public participation. X

© Stephen Pritchard
www.indexoncensorship.org

**Stephen Pritchard** is readers' editor at The Observer newspaper in the UK. He is a current board member and past president of the Organization of News Ombudsmen

# Print running

43(3): 51/54 | DOI: 10.1177/0306422014549148

Smart media operators have moved on from death-of-print debates to innovate for new audiences, says **Will Gore**, as more people consume journalism than ever before

**A**CCORDING TO THE old cliché, we get the press we deserve. In 2014 that means one which is still brilliant, still cynical but often delivered in bite-sized chunks or lists, and which is as likely to come via Twitter or Instagram as on newsprint.

Lately journalists have been on trial, literally and metaphorically. Ethics have been scrutinised and in some high-profile cases found wanting; working practices turned upside down by technological advances; employment imperilled by the general financial downturn. So what next?

In the UK, for instance, the print media has been in a state of flux for at least 15 years. The Society of Editors' annual conferences in the middle years of the last decade seemed perennially to include discussions about facing the future. For the most part there were more questions than answers.

It is clear that the historic decline in the readership of printed newspapers will not be reversed. The sales of UK national Sunday newspapers in June of this year was more or less half what they had been 10 years ago. With print advertising in the doldrums too, the inevitable response from most newspaper companies has been a contraction of editorial budgets.

Nevertheless, after a decade at the beginning of the century when there was more despair than action, the last five years have suggested that journalism can adapt to the modern world. Even in the print arena, innovation can bring rewards. The London Evening Standard, not a million miles from closure until Alexander and Evgeny Lebedev bought it and made it free in 2009, is now profitable and recently increased its circulation to 900,000. The i, introduced as a cut-price, stable-mate for The Independent, has increasingly gained a distinct identity, as well as a significant audience. And the average, combined circulation figures of the UK national dailies still stood at around 7.5 million in June.

The increasing dominance of the internet, which had seemed so threatening to traditional news business models, has ultimately provided opportunities as well. Even though the paywall versus free-access debate shows no sign of being resolved, arguably more people consume journalism now than at any time in the past. Its tone and content may divide opinion but the reach of Mail Online (well over 150 million unique monthly users) is hard to ignore, particularly when it is remembered that its group – Associated Newspapers – was a relative latecomer to web publishing. The Guardian, having been an early pioneer of the online realm, is now clearly identifiable as both an internet brand and a newsprint one.

But if the media industry feels like a more positive place now than it did 10 years →

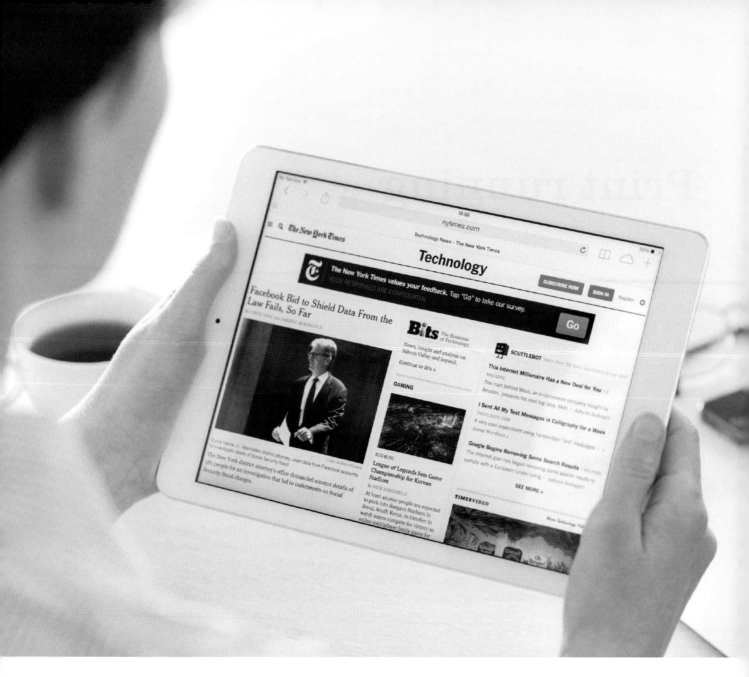

ABOVE: Print readership is in decline but newspapers are adapting to chase new audiences

→ ago, there is still a great deal of uncertainty about its future. In part this stems

## Social media is long enough in the tooth for us to know that it is not going to replace journalism

from a realisation that, just when traditional media companies had started to get to grips with the digital age, new players arrived at the table. Social media is long enough in the tooth for us to know that, for all its wonder, it is not going to replace journalism. But the success of Huffington Post and BuzzFeed have demonstrated two things: first, that online-only news and entertainment publishing can be successful; and second, that it is possible to gain a substantial web audience without having a print backstory.

Indeed, it can be advantageous to be a step away from the mainstream. That in part reflects the low esteem in which the dismissively termed "MSM" – mainstream media – appears to have been held by many in recent times.

The British press reached its nadir with the phone-hacking revelations that engulfed the News of the World three years ago. The subsequent Leveson inquiry exposed a lot of uncomfortable truths about the press in this country (as well as details about the nexus involving newspapers, politicians and elements of the police).

Yet the inquiry failed to draw a line under the debates that raged under its judicial auspices. In some respects that was perhaps inevitable. It was not, after all, able to look into the criminality that had led to its establishment (because of on-going cases) and many of the wider issues it examined were open to highly subjective analysis. Leveson's conclusions about press regulation were thought-provoking and his fundamental propositions – that self-regulation needed to be both independent and have some form of external oversight are hard to disagree with in principle. The problem is in the interpretation.

That both sides in the wrangling that has followed have sought to argue the toss about what is and is not Leveson-compliant (to borrow that awful *phrase du jour*) has been thoroughly depressing. It has had the result of reducing press regulation to points of (alleged) principle, while it is the practical impact on journalism and on the public that ought to define a regulator. One might wonder whether those who place so much store by Leveson's inquiry simply by virtue of its status felt the same about the Hutton inquiry into the events leading up to the war against Saddam Hussein, or any judicial inquiry for that matter. In the increasingly desperate, post-Leveson debate, dogma rules.

To a degree, regulation is frankly a red herring. The system operated by the Press Complaints Commission was not perfect but it was not – and I admittedly have an interest to declare as a former employee – the kind of complete failure that some have presented it as. But the question of what should succeed the PCC has become important because it

symbolises a much wider and more polarised discussion about what role "the press" or "the media" in Britain should play.

And fundamentally, it is the existence and nature of that debate which exemplifies, as much as any financial indicator, why journalism's future is important and potentially vulnerable.

Trust has, after all, emerged as the key conceptual battleground post-Leveson. There are those who would seek tougher regulation, prompted, they argue, by sections of the British press who have shown themselves utterly untrustworthy. On the other hand, for those who argue in favour of a lighter-touch system, trust in journalism is only possible when it is unencumbered by regulation that has any, even theoretical, link to the state. But these measures of trust are not

## Aspiring for a more accountable press is one thing; but it is often a short hop to intellectual snobbery and the dismissal of certain types of journalism

apolitical and can seem divorced from the day-to-practice of the trade.

For, while issues of trust may have been given a sharper focus by the hacking scandal, but it is the public's improved access to information online, and the role of social media which have been game-changers on a day-to-day basis. They have already allowed immediate – and often vocal – scrutiny of journalistic activity by citizens.

It is stating the obvious to say that mainstream media outlets are producing more content with fewer journalistic resources than at any previous time. The suggestion sometimes follows that this is a recipe for inaccurate and inadequate reporting. Yet with the instantaneous accountability that comes with Twitter-bombing or email →

→ campaigning, so there is no place for journalists to hide. As an experienced hand said to me recently, the days when journalists could take a few liberties because nobody else knew any better are long gone. And that is undeniably a good thing.

Yet formal campaigns for greater trust in the media (which often imagine a halcyon and imaginary time when journalists were held in high public regard) can create problems if they become intertwined with a desire for a different tone, as they seem sometimes to do. Aspiring for a more accountable press is one thing; but it is often a short hop to intellectual snobbery and to the subsequent dismissal of certain types of journalism wholesale.

The reality of the interaction between journalism and its audience is that it is predicated on myriad factors, not only trust and a mutual belief in the delivery and receipt of "proper" news. That was true 20 years ago; it is even more undeniable now.

When BuzzFeed started its life the focus was on fun. But it has since found space for more serious journalistic endeavour. The Daily Mail may be the kitchen-table read for conservative middle England; but Mail Online's sidebar of shame, despite its rather different style, still has a mass appeal. The Independent and The Guardian might promote the quality of their foreign news reportage, but there is room on their websites for amusing lists and videos.

Newspapers worked – and still work – because they had a mass appeal: news, comment, sport, puzzles, lifestyle tips, book reviews, and a lot else besides all in one place. The early response of publishers to the digital revolution was to forget that simple fact. Instead, the focus was often on replicating online the ideals that the print brand was known for, as if the purpose was to cater for the same audience via a different format. Only in the last five years have we seen the kind of online diversification which ought to have been the natural response of most publishers to having a potentially much wider reach.

Journalism's future is bright if it can be many things to many people. Trust is a part of that package and criminality is most definitely not – but neither of those concepts should become albatrosses that hinder innovation and expansion. X

© Will Gore
www.indexoncensorship.org

**Will Gore** is deputy managing editor of The Independent, i, Independent on Sunday and the London Evening Standard. He was formerly director of external affairs at the Press Complaints Commission. He tweets @ willjgore

# Paper chase

43(3): 55/58 | DOI: 10.1177/0306422014547672

Shortages of newsprint in Venezuela have forced newspapers to close, but online media are expanding fast to fill the gaps and bring the public the latest news. **Luis Carlos Díaz** reports from Caracas

EL IMPULSO, A Venezuelan newspaper with more than 110 years of history, announced its closure in May – not for the first time. There was a similar statement in January, and another in February. Each time, the journalists were hard at work, the pages were laid out and there was plenty of news. But one thing stopped the presses: no paper.

Venezuela has had paper shortages for the past two years. In 2013, 10 newspapers closed. Many more have shrunk in size. But digital news is taking up the slack.

Many newspapers have had to reassess their plans. El Correo del Caroni went from 32 pages to eight pages. El Nacional reduced its news coverage, cut its culture, sports sections, magazines and literary supplement. Even the pro-government Diario Vea announced several times that it was doomed (although it was later saved).

The internet has become the place where information from all over the country flows most freely and spontaneously. In Venezuela – a country of 29 million inhabitants – the internet reaches only 54 per cent of the population, but there has been a big growth in digital entrepreneurs as people try to attract new users. New sites include Poderopedia. org, launched in June by a disgruntled print journalist to investigate the links between politicians, business people and military officials.

SIC, the country's oldest magazine, run by a Jesuit political centre in Caracas, has decided to print at a loss this year as it works on a digitisation strategy. The magazine also has the challenge of trying to lure its subscribers (with an average age of 56) online. The key difference between Venezuela's media landscape and the rest of the world is that when people talk about the end of print journalism elsewhere, it is normally a discussion about changing technology; in Venezuela, it's different. The migration to digital platforms in Venezuela is a means of offsetting a crisis from a lack of physical paper.

It was Andiarios, a non-profit media organistaion from Colombia that saved El Impulso, by stepping in with an emergency paper delivery. "This allowed us to print for another month," says Carlos Eduardo Carmona, the newspaper's president. "We are still surviving day-by-day. Media managers feel like firefighters here, constantly controlling emergencies."

Inflation in Venezuela was already crippling (60 per cent was the official rate in 2013). But between June 2013 and January 2014, the cost of printing in Venezuela increased by 460 per cent.

The paper shortage is just one of many peculiarities of Venezuela. The oil-dependent economy has built a state with a chronic weakness at its heart. Little is produced →

ABOVE: Miguel Henrique Otero, president of El Nacional, talks to the media in front of a truck loaded with paper supplies at the newspaper's building in Caracas in April 2014. Demonstrators hold placards calling for the protection of a free press and free speech

Credit: Reuters/ Carlos Garcia Rawlins

→ domestically; almost everything is imported – including medicines, basic foods

## In 2013, 10 newspapers closed and many more have shrunk in size

and car parts. And these products can't be bought freely on the international market. All purchases have to go through the state – which creates a highly complicated system that leads to shortages.

A law on foreign exchange was passed by ex-president Hugo Chavez in 2003, meaning that only the government could administer the buying and selling of dollars. The government also has a list of priority goods for which it will grant dollars. But in August 2012, it decided to remove paper from the list, increasing the costs and the complications for anyone trying to import it.

The effect was not really felt until a year later, when it became apparent that paper supplies had dried up and a national toilet-paper shortage made international headlines. The damage to the newspaper industry, however, was long-lasting. The country's big newspapers reduced their pagination over the following six months, getting rid of whole sections and inserts.

Though the crisis really started with the government's 2012 decision, it was exacerbated by a succession of protests that began in February 2014. A series of youth demonstrations demanding the resignation of the government quickly escalated into violent clashes, in which 42 people died and more than 3,000 were arrested. In the weeks leading up to the protests, there were demonstrations by journalists and journalism students in Caracas, Barquisimeto and Ciudad Guayana, with an accompanying social media campaign. The Bloque de Prensa, an editors' alliance, estimated that there was a debt of at least US$15 million owed to suppliers.

The government responded by centralising paper purchasing, one day before the main protest. As a result, there is now only one entity that's authorised to buy paper from overseas – and all the newspapers and the country's editorial industry relies on it for their supplies.

Carmona, from El Impulso, says the state's paper supplier meets only half the paper's needs. Unlike other papers, he hasn't yet been pressured to change his oppositional editorial stance, but the size of the paper has shrunk, from 48 pages to 12 or 16. "We do not want to close, but neither do we want to be part of a Pyrrhic media with a limited presence. I no longer have space for reportage. We have cut out information, decreased the font size and line spacing. We have fewer photos. The news is telegraphic and worse quality. But at least we're still running."

Official statistics on dollar purchases from January to April 2014 reveal that US $7.41 million was approved for paper for the media. And 85 per cent of this amount ($ 6.3 million) was intended for Últimas Noticias, the newspaper with the biggest circulation in the country, which was bought in 2013 with capital linked to the national government.

After the buyout, Últimas Noticias changed in its editorial stance to favour the government. Many of its main journalists have since either quit in protest or been fired.

Miguel Henrique Otero is editor-in-chief of El Nacional, currently the only oppositional newspaper in Caracas, after El Universal was sold in July. He says: "The government knows perfectly well what the newspapers' needs are. They know they approved currency to buy paper, yet they don't pay out for unknown reasons, which one assumes are political. All they need to do is buy a media network, one that bows down to them, so that the money starts to flow."

Mariaengracia Chirinos, a communications researcher and a member of Venezuela's Press and Society Institute, believes the

## We have cut out information. The news is telegraphic and worse quality

shortage of paper affects the readers more than the companies: "Information now comes in half-measures. It has to resort to other spaces and self-publishing, which is sometimes a good thing, but when it is a response to restrictions, it can also affect the citizen's ability to choose where they get their information from."

Polarisation have been strong in Venezuela since the coup d'etat of 2002, but the last election in 2013, after the death of divisive leader Hugo Chavez, further increased the frustration of opposition activists because they disputed the result (the margin of victory for Nicolás Maduro being just being 1.49 per cent). Fernando Giuliani, a social psychologist, says: "Polarisation is so strong that state media do not have any room for opposition issues, either in news or in opinion. We have broken bridges and now there is no more room for dialogue."  →

|||||||||||||||||||||||||||||||||||||||||||||||||

## How Venezuela's economy works

A law controlling currency exchange was set up by then-president Hugo Chavez in 2003, meaning that only the government can administer the buying and selling of dollars because they come from the state-owned oil industry. It was intended to avoid capital flight and to control the prices of food staples. By maintaining dollars at a subsidised price, it is cheaper to import products than to produce them in the country.

Currently Venezuela has four exchange rates: the Tasa Cencoex at 6,30 bolívares to the dollar (for state imports only); the Tasa Sicad 1 at 10 bolívares to the dollar (in state-controlled sales for companies); the Tasa Sicad 2 at 50 bolívares to the dollar (in state-controlled sales for citizens); and the black market rate, from 65 to 80 bolívares to the dollar – an unofficial, illegal rate that is nevertheless common on the streets. The state has tried to centralise all the economic variables, but it hasn't gone well.

→ What Venezuela needs most is the establishment of information channels that are both reliable and successful in increasing public loyalty. For the Venezuelan media, it's more about quantity of readers than quality of content, because costs are too high. Today every digital user in the country is left navigating the complex media scene by themselves, working out how to process information and working their way through a hierarchy of networks. What we have is not enough to know about all that's going on, but it is empowering citizens to make choices for themselves. ⌧

© Luis Carlos Díaz
www.indexoncensorship.org

*Translated by Clemmy Manzo*

**Luis Carlos Díaz** is a Venezuelan journalist, based in Caracas

# Lobby matters

43(3): 59/62 | DOI: DOI: 10.1177/0306422014547477

Political reporting in Britain has been criticised for being incestuous and outdated. But, argues **Ian Dunt**, spending time and money on a story is the only way to discover secrets

**A**BOVE THE CHAMBER of the House of Commons in London, there's a maze of little decrepit hallways and offices that constitute the parliamentary lobby. It is a very odd and misunderstood place, but it is where the leading political journalists work. The name doesn't help – people from overseas usually assume membership is akin to corporate lobbying. At home, it is not much better understood, even among the well-informed.

As with most British institutions, it is creaky, in a state of disrepair and full of ideas that are worth preserving. The most important of these is that independent journalists should be embedded in the centre of political power.

The lobby gives journalists privileged access to the prime minister's spokesperson who does a question-and-answer session each morning and afternoon, not unlike those rapidly edited scenes in the US TV series The West Wing, except with more gloominess and less forward momentum. Until 2000, these sessions were off-the-record and – before my time – you used actually to learn things. Nowadays they are on-the-record and rarely reveal anything that wasn't intended for publication.

The invited journalists' skills include a heightened ability to interpret the motives and consequences of particular words. They use this in a game with the spokesman to prise out nuggets of useful information. The atmosphere is one of mutual understanding, against a backdrop of systemic animosity. For the spokesman, it is a very delicate operation. The slightest ill-advised turn of phrase can lead the news headlines within minutes.

There is a good-humoured, collegiate attitude in the lobby – both among journalists and between them and politicians – which makes the daily brutality of politics somewhat easier to bear. Partly this is a result of the fact that lobby journalists have escaped their boss. They are regularly hassled by the news desk, of course, but it is remarkable what it will do for someone's disposition to arrange some geographical distance from the management.

The proximity of members of parliament makes it easier to create and maintain contacts. But it also plays a symbolic role. Many MPs would love to move the lobby out of parliament and across the river, or possibly dump it in it. They hate having journalists freely walking around parliament. This discomfort is a barometer of how useful the lobby's constitutional function is. As a rule of thumb, a comfortable politician is a bad one.

Very recently, digital news outlets, including the one I run, started to be allowed in (2009, in our case). This was a strange moment for the parliamentary →

ABOVE: A BBC television crew film outside the Houses of Parliament in London

it will not hold for long. Too many major players in the online world are outside the lobby system. It does them comparatively little damage. It does the lobby system rather a lot, because it makes it seem ancient and ill-suited to the modern media climate. This is a criticism that even its most committed defender would have to accept.

For many, the lobby system has become a symbol of journalists' connivance with MPs. The relationships in some places are too close, but that is a human problem pertinent to any kind of journalism. To know things, you must get close to people. But by getting close to them you sometimes find you rather like them and then seek to protect them. It is a philosophical quandary, not a modern one. The solution – admittedly a limited one – is to separate the staff who are intended to make friends with contacts from those who screw them.

But the thrust of the criticism is accurate. There is something undeniably establishment about the lobby. It sometimes feels as if someone has offered you a pair of slippers, a fireplace and a copy of the Daily Telegraph. Only the most psychologically damaged of 30-year-olds would find that an attractive proposition. But as you age it becomes more seductive. Eventually, you might empathise more with your contacts than your readers.

The lobby system has also been partially undone by technology. Being able to question the prime minister's spokesman is a luxury. But the demands of daily online journalism make it a demanding one. It's 40 minutes away from the desk, twice a day, all so you can receive a drip of information that will be tweeted by your colleagues as soon as it is said.

It has also been used and abused by political parties. As newspapers' and broadcasters' resources dwindle and staff numbers are reduced, journalists have found themselves ever more reliant on party press offices for their stories. Smart Downing Street

→ authorities. On the one hand they had to recognise changing consumer habits. On

## The atmosphere is one of mutual understanding, against a backdrop of systemic animosity

the other, there had to be a reason for some blogs to be allowed in and others not. There is still an uneasy truce over admissions, but

Credit: Justin Kase z11z/ Alamy

communications officials will keep stories in their back pocket for journalists as a reward, or to dampen a damaging story. It is not dissimilar to the way you treat a child. In Westminster, the Conservative Party press office is particularly effective at feeding journalists stories about their opponents.

After the second leader's debate of the 2010 general election, for instance, Liberal Democrat leader Nick Clegg was temporarily the subject of huge public acclaim. His polling went through the roof and even started to nudge up against that of the leaders of the two much larger parties. People got nervous. Suddenly there appeared in the press an extraordinary range of attacks, overwhelmingly originating in opposition Conservative party HQ, about the man who would later become deputy prime minister. His expenses were questioned, as was his employment record. The Daily Mail even used his multicultural background to observe that he was "by blood the least British leader of a British political party".

A similar campaign was deployed against another party, Ukip, ahead of this year's local and European elections and will be deployed again against Ed Miliband's Labour Party in the upcoming general election.

Of course, journalists and editors should always be wary of being used as a political party's meat puppet. The fact that the political departments of various newspapers are working side-by-side also has drawbacks. It encourages, even among very different newspapers, a pack mentality. It is a homogenising force in an industry that prides itself on its variety. The internet has made it easier to break away from this trend, because it has revealed a ready audience for serious news stories outside the mainstream cycle. But many know no other way.

The biggest obstacle the lobby faces does not come from politicians, or even from its own internal contradictions, but from readers. Increasingly, the public has lost interest in Westminster. And without Westminster,

the lobby is nothing but a wild animal with nothing to eat.

British politics has become fixated with the 100,000 or so swing voters who decide an election. As all three main parties hone in relentlessly on that middle ground, the grand ideological narratives of politics are being lost, to be replaced by nuggets of focus-group-approved policy and personal power struggles.

This resulted in years of hostile press briefing between Tony Blair and Gordon Brown, two men who had fewer political differences than most people have children. Yet somehow this battle of personalities – one telegenic and half-crazed, the other dour and wooden – dominated British political life for

# You can get more traffic from a celebrity rumour than from sending a correspondent to the corridors of power

a decade. Newspaper readers, like many voters, decided that wasn't for them.

Then there is the uncomfortable reality of Westminster's declining relevance. Multinational corporations wield far more power, as do transnational institutions like the EU. Many of the most significant political events of the last decade came not from elected politicians but relatively small non-state actors like al-Qaeda or Occupy.

This loss of interest in Westminster has coincided with the internet's destruction of journalism's financial model. There is less money for lawyers. There is less money for staff, so the remaining journalists are rigorously overworked. And there is more data available on readers' habits, all of which suggests that you could get more traffic regurgitating a celebrity rumour than from sending out dedicated correspondents to the corridors of power. Increasingly, editors →

→ are sending inexperienced staff to the lobby or just picking up political news off the wires.

The natural endpoint of this type of business model was expressed by David Montgomery, chief executive of Local World, which owns several local newspapers across the UK. The "human interface" involved in local news publishing would disappear within four years, he said in 2013. The "content harvesting process" would invite police forces, for instance, to publish their own press releases on local news sites. Montgomery seemed unaware, or unwilling to be aware, of why this would not provide effective scrutiny of authorities. It's a nightmare vision of political journalism.

For all its faults, the lobby represents a barrier against that type of coverage. It is the journalism of time and money, where reporters are sent somewhere and given time to discover secrets and where editors have the funds and inclination to face down legal threats.

Undoubtedly the lobby needs to change, to expand its coverage and broaden its membership. But it can't be given up on. Establishment or not, it puts the fear in politicians. And that alone should commend it. ☒

© Ian Dunt
www.indexoncensorship.org

**Ian Dunt** is editor of politics.co.uk

# Funding news freedom

43(3): 63/66 | DOI: 10.1177/0306422014548376

If high-quality, research-based journalism is going survive, someone is going to have pay for it. **Glenda Nevill** explores some innovative projects using unusual ways to pay for reporting

THE BLUEPRINT FOR funding 21st-century journalism is still being drawn. The details are sketchy, but it is clear the current model is hopelessly out-of-date and out-of-touch with the reality of digital evolution. The upheaval has paralysed some media houses and given others the impetus both to revisit not just how journalism is practised, but to reinvent the whole concept of news, how it is delivered and how it is funded.

Julie Posetti, an Australian journalist and journalism lecturer now working as a research fellow at the World Editors Forum and the World Association of Newspapers and News Publishers (Wan-Ifra), says that the global publishing industry is in the midst of a "seemingly never-ending stage of upheaval and reinvention" when it comes to journalism business models.

"The shift from reliance on the traditional advertising model has been slow and painful in some sections of the industry, with Western developed countries, in particular, suffering a huge blow as the tidal wave of convergent crises hit. These include the collapse in advertising, the rise of interactive digital media, and reducing trust in journalists following various scandals. The impacts have included the closure of many publications and the sacking of more journalists globally," she says.

But this is a period of transition in which new forms of journalism and publication methods are being developed, along with new business models. "We don't know yet what a sustainable 21st-century news business model will look like, but it is likely to involve a combination of philanthropic backing, crowdfunding, collaborations between journalists and non-profit organisations, universities, and traditional advertising," Posetti says.

There are three things we do know for sure, she says. "Firstly, there remains a very strong appetite for investigative journalism in the public interest. Secondly, video drives advertising sales (and traffic), and thirdly, this is an evolutionary process."

While the appetite for investigative journalism might be strong, it isn't always sated by a matching investment in the labour-intensive and expensive craft.

Francois Pierre Nel, director of the Journalism Leaders' Programme at the School of Journalism and Media at the University of Central Lancashire in the UK, says that tying the future of journalism to the future of legacy media organisations "would be a mistake".

He believes there are several reasons why investigative journalism has a bright future. "Traditional media companies, struggling to find ways of distinguishing themselves in the intensely competitive digital landscape, are increasingly establishing hubs to work →

ABOVE: Dutch news site De Correspondent has used crowdfunding to pay for its journalism

→ data-driven content, including investigative reporting. Investigative efforts are being funded by concerned individual philanthropists and groups."

In South Africa, the respected Mail & Guardian newspaper has a separate centre for investigative journalism, AmaBhugane (which means "dung beetles" and which led to its quirky tagline, "Digging dung. Fertilising democracy"). Founded by Stefaans Brummer and Sam Sole in 2010, it has been responsible for some powerful stories, including investigations into massive state spending of R246 million ($22 million) on President Jacob Zuma's private home in Nkandla, KwaZulu-Natal.

Brummer says AmaBhugane, by necessity, has an arm's length relationship with the Mail & Guardian. "There's a misconception that the M&G owns AmaBhugane, which creates problems. AmaBhugane is a non-profit, and cannot be owned by anyone."

Donor funding supports AmaBhugane. The M&G pays just one-third of its costs, which mainly goes towards salaries. The operation has 12 staff members, including three interns. It has three main pillars: investigations, advocacy and skills transfer.

"We set out to create conditions in which investigative journalism could thrive," says Brummer. "We operate on a budget of R8 million ($754,658) and are supported by six donors, other than the M&G." These include the Open Society Foundation for South Africa, the Open Society Initiative for Southern Africa, the Raith Foundation, the Bertha Foundation, the Millennium Trust and the Claude Leon Foundation.

The Claude Leon Foundation, says Brummer, pays AmaBhugane's legal costs – not for defending their stories, but rather for advocacy work such as challenges to the Public Access to Information Acts. In the case of Nkandla, the unit went to court to access more than 12,000 pages of documents that helped uncover the scale of state spending on the president's home. But it cost over R700,000 ($66,031) to get the documents.

Posetti says that in many cases, donor funding can be precarious. "There is no doubt that we are facing a more vulnerable future as individual journalists and publications – more akin to the experience of artists, start-ups, community organisations and theatre companies. But as the need and demand for quality investigative journalism continue, we will find a way to keep producing. 'We are like the proverbial cockroaches', said Janine Gibson, editor-in-chief of The Guardian's online operation in the US, when asked about the future of investigative journalists, in an interview for the Trends in Newsrooms report. I think she's right. And the result of this precariousness may also result in highly creative, innovative journalism."

The success of De Correspondent would certainly fit the mould of creative, innovative journalism. The Dutch online newspaper is entirely funded by its readers, or rather "members", as the title prefers to call them. Its founders, Rob Wijnberg and Ernst-Jan Pfauth, were both editors at a newspaper in Holland. Wijnberg, then editor of NRC Handelsblad, in the face of free online media, wanted to move the editorial focus of the newspaper from "news" to "new". "New," says Pfauth, meant "reporting on the kinds of developments that are less spectacular than most news events, but that do have a large impact on our daily lives."

To make it happen Harald Dunnink from creative agency Momkai said he could build a platform for a cost price if 15,000 people paid at least €60 ($80) each via a crowdfunding campaign. Wijberg wrote a manifesto in which he promised to "to uncover, explain and highlight deep-lying structures and long-term developments that powerfully shape our world, rather than speculating about the latest hype, scare, or breaking news story". He appeared on TV and in eight days raised €1 million ($1.3 million) to fund the venture. De Correspondent launched in September 2013, with 20,000 members and now has nearly 34,000, each paying €60 ($80) a year. The site is free of advertising. This approach – analysis, background pieces and investigative reporting – had found favour with many readers of NRC Handelsblad's under Wijnberg's editorship, so much so that many cancelled their subscriptions when Wijnberg left, and became founding members of De Correspondent.

Germany's Krautreporter soon followed. Describing itself as a daily magazine telling stories behind the news, it is "ad-free, made for the internet and founded by its readers". The writers, around 30 journalists, say they "no longer want to wait for big media companies to allow true journalism on the net. We are all working for years as journalists with great commitment to the established media. And we believe: now it's time for something new". They met, and exceeded, their goal of 15,000 investors contributing €5 a month ($6.6), or €60 ($80) a year. In July, 17,545 investors had contributed to their crowdfunding cause.

Contributoria.com, born out of a Google/IPI news innovation competition, is an independent journalism community whose members collaborate on all aspects of the writing process, including commissioning, editing and publication. Sarah Hartley, one of the founders, says: "In the team, we describe

it as a community crowdfunding model. Externally, we've also been described as the offspring that would result from Kickstarter and Medium."

Members join the platform and their fees contribute to a funding pool. Writers propose story ideas, which are moderated, and the community chooses which pitches to fund each month. The successful stories are published in Contributoria's magazine, but can also be sold.

Hartley, with The Guardian's Matt McAlister, and Dan Catt, one of the developers of Flickr, founded Contributoria to "utilise the opportunities technology provides for group

# Individual journalists and publications are facing a more vunerable future – akin to artists and start-ups

action and support in the interest of quality journalism". It went live in January 2014.

"The first challenge was being able to explain the concept to people. The whole idea of crowdfunding was less familiar to people when we first started developing the idea in 2009-10," says Hartley. "It wasn't as much a technical limitation as a cultural one. The different methods that technologies have made possible was something more familiar to the tech world than to the rather risk-averse environment of journalism.

"The most recent challenge has been the introduction of the payment mechanism to allow members of the community to get involved in the ongoing funding of the platform. This launched in July and was a major landmark for us in terms of both technical development and our future financial security."

Hartley says Contributoria.com has developed revenue streams to supplement the paid, community-membership model. →

||||||||||||||||||||||||||||||||||||||||||||||||||||||||||||||

# India's news spin-off

·············································

*Indian news service Newslaundry is hoping viewers who want investigative, independent reporting will help fund its work*

Website Newlaundry is a new type of news service in India. The founders, Madhu Trehan, Prashant Sareen, Roopak Kapoor and Abhinandan Sekhri, are using an alternative model to fund journalism, research and investigative reporting in India. They are using an ad-free platform, which is funded by viewers and supporters.

Sekhri, a writer for satirical news shows including Great Indian Tamasha, says: "Given the reach, spend and circumstances in which we rolled out our I Pay To Keep News Free Campaign, I'd say we've been very successful. I am thrilled and encouraged. I think given the right positioning this is a model that has a bright future. So far we have only put up a payment gateway for people to pay [from 100 rupees – around £1 – per month.] Going forward we will be creating innovative spaces and creating partnerships and collaborations for people to get involved and support Newslaundry, which right now seem rather radical to many, but given our experience it can work very well."

He thinks the world will see this type of funding as the next step. "I think this is the future of journalism. The transition from state-funded to ad-funded was the first transition and ad funded to collaborative and reader/viewer driven and funded is the next big step. In the future, ad-funded models will still exist but viewer-funded will be the standard."

→  "These include sponsorship of particular magazine editions; so far we've partnered with organisations such as the United Nations Development Programme and the International Press Institute."

Matthew Buckland, a South African digital media entrepreneur, online publisher and owner of digital agency Creative Spark (which publishes Memeburn, Ventureburn and Gearburn), believes "advertising will still be a key revenue stream for most commercial media companies in the future".

"I think it's a mistake to think that print titles will wane in the face of the digital revolution. I argue they will do just the opposite. As a result of digital information overload and too many choices, I predict print will see a big comeback and it is a good business model for certain niches and publications." Buckland says digital publications are still searching for "an optimal online advertising model". A resurgence of print and an improvement on the online advertising model "should see an improvement for the media industry in general".

As Posetti says, the funding models of the future are in a trial-and-error phase. "But in that process we are starting to see patterns emerging that should help guide the development of business models – such as the trend to the very short and live, and the very long and deep as sustainable forms of journalism." X

© Glenda Nevill
www.indexoncensorship.org

**Glenda Nevill** worked for South Africa's Sunday Times for nine years, including as a foreign correspondent. She is currently editor of The Media Online and is based in Cape Town. She tweets @glendaN

# Global view

43(3): 67/69 | DOI: 10.1177/0306422014548387

New British play Making Stalin Laugh explores the work of the Moscow State Yiddish Theatre before the company was closed and its actors executed. Index on Censorship's CEO **Jodie Ginsberg** looks at why artists are often on the front line of censorship battles

**"I**F **[MY PLAY]** gets a bad review, then that will be disappointing and may affect sales and my dream of an Olivier Award. But a bad review for Goset [the Moscow State Yiddish Theatre] could literally be a death sentence," wrote British writer David Schneider of Making Stalin Laugh, his play about the theatre company that battled for more than a quarter of a century, sometimes literally, to stay alive as it negotiated the terrors of Stalinist Russia and World War II.

Schneider was not exaggerating. In 1948, Solomon Mikhoels, Goset's leading actor and director, was murdered on government's orders. The authorities shut down the group and four years later its remaining members were executed. Up until then they'd walked a tightrope, adjusting constantly for about-turns of government taste, while trying to stay true to their values – and entertain. "Even a long-running hit could suddenly be denounced as 'counter-revolutionary', striking panic into all concerned," wrote Schneider in UK newspaper The Guardian, ahead of his play's June debut in at London's JW3 theatre.

Nearly 70 years on, and 23 years since the collapse of the Soviet Union, it can sometimes be easy to forget the power of the artist in challenging repression, or the conditions of fear and terror under which many of them work. Repressive governments know the power that writers and artists can wield. That is why, even in the internet age, they seek to censor and control artistic expression.

Lebanese writer Lucien Bourjeily made censorship the theme of his latest play – Will it Pass or Not? – to test the limits of a law that has created a "climate of fear" in his country. "Because the censorship law in Lebanon is so vague and elusive," he told Index earlier this year, artworks that might have received approval two years ago are censored or banned today. "In this climate of fear, the military obviously becomes more present in day-to-day life, tightening security … and tightening their grip on freedom of expression … Censorship thrives when the state feels insecure or when it makes the common mistake of correlating security and freedom of expression." Bourjeily's play was banned and, in May, authorities confiscated his passport – although they later returned it.

Many artists face harassment and imprisonment for work that questions the apparatus of the state. Index condemned Morocco's government, for example, over the trial of rapper Mouad Belghouat – also known as Lhaqed or El Haqed, "the →

ABOVE: Making Stalin Laugh, by David Schneider, was performed at the JW3 theatre in London in June and July 2014

→ enraged one" – who was sentenced in July to four months in prison. Belghouat, accused of assaulting police officers, was

## Years after the Soviet Union's collapse, it can be easy to forget the power of the artist in challenging repression

convicted following proceedings that defence lawyers called "unjust" and "unfair", and which rights groups believe were intended to

punish the popular musician for lyrics that condemn corruption and police brutality.

Governments fear these artists because in many countries, it is these very individuals who are among the most powerful advocates for change, articulating frustrations that state and private media can or will not address. Such governments ban anything, and anyone, that might challenge the official narrative, on the pretext of ensuring national stability, of maintaining law and order.

In Egypt, for example, artistic expression is playing a key role in challenging the rising tide of sexual violence against women.

Though the government has introduced belated legislation to tackle these crimes, their efforts are seen as weak and ineffectual. Anger at the inability of the police, government and judiciary to deal with sexual violence is being channelled into art. Through plays, street art, music and dance, men and women are addressing an issue that gets little coverage in the traditional media. "Art is one of the most necessary mediums to impact society," says Deena Mohamed, who created a web comic about a hijab-wearing superhero fighting daily sexual harassment. "For people who are unaware of the issues women go through, I hope it helps them understand or at least gives them something to think about."

Visual art and the spoken word also take on added importance in areas where literacy levels are low and internet access is poor. In Burma, before the political reforms that started at the end of 2011, writers would hold talks about literary classics, which masked discussion of current affairs and political commentary. But while artists have the power to rattle governments, they are also vulnerable. Authors, poets, playwrights, painters and sculptors work largely alone. They are not salaried, they lack the security that being part of a large, or even small, company can offer. And without public recognition, they are often seen as easy targets by repressive regimes. That is why it is crucial that these individuals, and their works, are championed. Without them, we are all diminished. ☒

© Jodie Ginsberg
www.indexoncensorship.org

**Jodie Ginsberg** is the CEO of Index on Censorship

ABOVE: Soldiers from Australia's North West Mobile Force, a surveillance unit that employs ancient Aboriginal skills

**IN FOCUS**

In this section

# Free thinking?

43(3): 70/74 | DOI: 10.1177/0306422014548630

Australian Race Commissioner **Tim Soutphommasane** argues that the right to be a bigot should not override the right to be free from the effects of bigotry

**M**ANY SAY FREEDOM of expression means nothing if it doesn't entail a freedom to offend others. Enjoying such →

→ freedom means that you may also have to tolerate hurtful or distasteful speech. But what if the burden of tolerance is not borne equally? What if some forms of speech wound not merely sensibilities but also another person's dignity? How should a liberal democracy treat forms of speech that degrade others because of their race?

Since 1995, Australian law has prohibited acts of racial vilification in public. This legal protection against racism was a response to mounting community concern about racist abuse and violence. For most of the past two decades, the law has been a source of little controversy, and accepted as part of the legislative expression of Australian multiculturalism.

## The federal government argues its amendment would enhance freedom of speech, but there has been overwhelming public opposition to the mooted change

Yet the vilification provisions of the federal Racial Discrimination Act (1975) have recently been subject to intense debate. During last year's election campaign, the then Liberal-National conservative opposition pledged to repeal the part of the act concerned with vilification. Then the conservatives won the election. Subsequently, in March this year, the federal government released a draft of proposed amendments to the act.

The federal government argued its proposed amendment would enhance freedom of speech, but there was overwhelming public opposition to the mooted change. An opinion poll in April showed that 88 per cent of Australians believed the law should stay as it is. Aboriginal and ethnic community groups, along with human rights organisations, have expressed their serious concern

that amending the law may have the effect of licensing racial hatred. Remarks by the federal attorney-general endorsing a "right to be a bigot" appear only to have confirmed such anxiety.

In August, the federal government backed down on its planned reforms. Prime Minister Tony Abbott said he was making a "leadership call" not to proceed with the proposed changes. Abbott said: "I want to work with the communities of our country as Team Australia."

This has been a strange debate. No compelling reason was put forward for changing the law. There was little public clamour for reform, even if influential sections of the Australian media were stirred by a *cause célèbre* in 2011 involving conservative newspaper columnist Andrew Bolt. Following articles written about "air-skinned" Aboriginal people, Bolt was found to have contravened the Racial Discrimination Act.

Section 18c of the act makes it unlawful to "offend, insult, humiliate or intimidate" another person on racial or ethnic grounds in public (religion isn't an attribute covered by the law). This is balanced by section 18d, which protects anything that is done as artistic work, scientific inquiry or fair comment and reporting – provided it is done reasonably and in good faith. In Bolt's case, the court found that he didn't enjoy this broad protection of fair comment because he had combined factual errors and inflammatory language.

Much public commentary has misleadingly referred to Bolt being "prosecuted" and "convicted" under the act. Unlike laws concerning racial vilification elsewhere, however, Australian federal discrimination law isn't criminal in nature. It merely provides for civil and educative remedies for racial discrimination. People who believe they have experienced unlawful discrimination can make a complaint, which then proceeds to conciliation conducted by the Australian Human Rights Commission. Only when conciliation fails may a complainant take the matter to court (which occurs rarely).

The operation of the law aside, there are questions about the philosophical principles concerning free speech.

There is clear community recognition of one thing: free speech is not absolute. But where the line is drawn is rightly open to contention. Under the current law, the limits are drawn at acts which "offend, insult, humiliate or intimidate" on racial grounds. Proponents of section 18c's repeal argue that there is a chilling effect in making offensive or insulting speech unlawful.

If this were the case under the current law, that would be a problem that warrants attention. But the courts have interpreted the law only to be concerned with those acts that cause "serious and profound effects" as opposed to "mere slights". In other words, the law sets the bar much higher than trivial offence or hurt feelings on the grounds of race. The courts have also given a broad interpretation of the free speech exemption currently enjoyed under section 18d. Numerous complaints involving people being offended or insulted on racial grounds by artistic works or political opinion have failed.

The federal government's proposed reforms drew the line in a manner that not many Australians agree is appropriate. Namely, it proposed that only acts that incite racial hatred or physically intimidate on racial grounds be made unlawful. Anything that is done when participating in "public discussion", meanwhile, would be protected speech.

This combination would have done more than of prohibited conduct; it would have removed the requirements of reasonableness and good faith in the law's current free speech exemption. It isn't clear what, if any, conduct would be unlawful. Those who conduct themselves dishonestly or in bad faith would be protected from being held accountable for racial vilification. For example, virulent anti-semitism and Holocaust denial – which have been found to contravene the existing law – would likely have been protected speech under the federal government's proposals, given they could be justified as public discussion. Many forms of racial abuse in public would likely have been beyond the reach of a complaint, unless it could be demonstrated they could incite a third party to racial hatred or cause direct physical intimidation.

Those favouring an absolutist view of free speech may invoke the wisdom of John Stuart Mill: there "ought to exist the fullest liberty of professing and discussing, as a matter of conviction, any doctrine, however immoral it may be considered". Only where there is incitement of physical harm, it could be argued, are we justified in limiting speech. Furthermore, where there is "bad speech" –

## A weakening of current laws may have the effect of emboldening a minority to believe they can racially abuse others with impunity

including racist hate speech – we should rely on the marketplace of ideas to sort it out.

A liberal understanding of free speech, however, should always be placed in context. Even for a seminal defender of free speech such as Mill, the defence of liberty was ultimately concerned with the value of individuality. Free speech mattered for Mill not just because it enabled the discovery of truth, but also because it was necessary for self-realisation.

This point about individuality is important. Hearing wrong and distasteful views is one thing – but what if hearing those views has the effect of distorting a person's individuality? What if the expression of such views has the effect of silencing others? Would a →

→ Millian liberalism endorse hate-speech if it harmed another person's ability to realise his or her potential as an individual?

In any debate about racism and freedom of speech, we should remember that one of the profound effects of racist abuse is that it diminishes those who are its targets. Racism can make people feel unsafe in public places. It can also make it more difficult for people to exercise their own freedom of speech.

Indeed, this is one reason why it seems limiting to confine the task of combating bad speech with good speech. Social power matters. More speech can be easy to prescribe if you are an articulate and well-educated professional or someone accustomed to enjoying social privilege. But it would be unrealistic to expect that the speech of the strong can be countered by the speech of the vulnerable. Not everyone is in a position of parity

## It would be unrealistic to expect that the speech of the strong can be countered by the speech of the vunerable

to speak back. In any case, you can't assume that racism can be countered by a well-reasoned riposte. Those perpetuating racism mightn't be persuaded to change their mind through reason – simply because racism isn't rational in the first place.

It is for these reasons that the law can play an important role in striking the proper balance between freedom of speech and freedom from racial discrimination. In a liberal democracy, we value free speech because it is tied to the dignity of the individual. If that is the case, we should also recognise that some forms of speech can inflict serious harms on others.

The law, of course, cannot on its own ever eradicate racial discrimination. But it can reflect and promote social values; after all, it regulates many aspects of life, serving

to shape people's conduct and behaviour. In the area of speech, it is striking that for all of the existing suite of legislation that restricts expression – in national security, communications, trade practices, and public order – so much attention has lately been placed on a provision that was introduced to provide a civil remedy for those subjected to racial abuse and harassment.

The strong support for the current Racial Discrimination Act affirms Australian society's deep commitment to racial tolerance. It affirms that Australians not only value living in a society that condemns racism, but that they believe it is right that their laws reflect their values – that the law should play a part in setting a civil tone in a liberal democratic society. Quite rightly, there was concern that a weakening of current laws may have the effect of emboldening a minority to believe they can racially abuse others with impunity.

It was a welcome move from the Prime Minister to abandon the proposed reform of the act. While debates about race can often divide more than unite, the contest over section 18c has united Australians in one sense. The vast majority of Australians agree that a right to be a bigot must not outweigh a right to be free from bigotry's effects. ☒

© Tim Soutphommasane
www.indexoncensorship.org

**Tim Soutphommasane** is Australia's race discrimination commissioner and he tweets @timsout

# Guarding the guards

43(3): 75/78 | DOI: 10.1177/0306422014548359

Chinese lawyers who defend cases for free speech and are increasingly using social media to highlight issues often find themselves targets, reports **Jemimah Steinfeld**

**T**HIS YEAR HAS not been a good one for human rights lawyers in China. The biggest blow came in June, when, after a month in detention, human rights lawyer Pu Zhiqiang was arrested. Pu, who is a major symbol of the movement for political and legal reform inside China, was charged with "creating a disturbance" and "illegally obtaining personal information". His arrest came just days after he attended a private commemoration of the 25th anniversary of the Tiananmen Square massacre. Supporters say these charges are an attempt to silence the lawyer and others who might speak out.

Another high profile case occurred a few months earlier. Four lawyers were believed to have been beaten and detained after visiting an illegal detention centre in Jiamusi, Heilongjiang province, according to reports in the local media. Maya Wang, a researcher from Human Rights Watch, tells Index: "These lawyers have been fighting for years. Despite talk of progress we still have cases of people trying to protect others who are beaten by law enforcement officials. That's the picture of where we are today. They keep up the fight, but the current situation is pretty grim."

These two examples are just the ones that have made their way into the press; many more go unreported. As we approach the two-year anniversary of Xi Jinping coming to power in November 2012, crackdowns of this nature are becoming commonplace,

and indicate where China is when it comes to free speech. Any hope that Xi"s administration would be more tolerant of dissent appear to have been dashed. A common, bleak joke now circulates: "Even lawyers" lawyers need lawyers."

"A lot of the trends identified in our 2011 report still exist or have worsened," Amnesty International China researcher William Nee explains to Index. "Xi's administration seems to want to monopolise the political and legal system, which puts human rights lawyers in a difficult situation."

In many ways human rights lawyers are part of the story of China's recent economic success. The legal profession barely featured in China's imperial past and was largely banned under Mao. When Mao Zedong died in 1976, the seeds of the Chinese legal profession today were planted.

Still, 30 years ago China only had a handful of law schools and there were no more than 1,000 law graduates each year. These lawyers were considered state workers. As the years passed, this started to change. A degree of autonomy ensued. The total number of practicing lawyers in China jumped from 8,571 in 1981 to around 230,000 in 2013, and a small, but growing, proportion of these (around 300 today) have concentrated on human rights.

Lawyers have made tremendous strides in recent years. They have largely moved →

浦志強

獨立評論人協會
INDEPENDENT COMMENTATORS ASSOCIATION

謹自況蓋

高瑜

ABOVE: Protesters carry portraits of Chinese human rights lawyer Pu Zhiqiang and journalist Gao Yu at a march in Hong Kong in July 2014

out of the shadows of the government. This sadly comes at a price. As human rights lawyers gain more autonomy, the backlash is significant.

"Five to six years ago they targeted only a very small number of lawyers, but now dozens of lawyers have been affected," says Victor Clemens from The Network of Chinese Human Rights Defenders, a coalition of Chinese and international human rights non-governmental organisations.

Index spoke to lawyer Jin Guanghong, who was forced to flee China for fear of his life. Jin first encountered hostility back in the late 1990s, when teaching at Xiamen University. He was considered too radical and removed from his post. He got his lawyer's licence in 2008 and went on to represent a Falun Gong practitioner, Sun Xianglian from Zhejiang province. Members of Falun Gong, a Chinese spiritual practise, earned themselves illegal status when they spoke out against the government. This was Jin's first human rights case and led him onto many more. That was until 8 April 2011, after he acted in defence of a Falun Gong family in Guangzhou. He was arrested, and disappeared until 19 April. Due to the brutal abuse he tells us he received, he has lost some of his memory. Jin has memories of being picked up by police while walking down the street. He was held in a detention centre and later a mental hospital. In the hospital, he was beaten, given injections and drugs, and force-fed. He only has vague recollections of all of this. At the end of the ordeal, three teachers from Xiamen University and his brother were sent to pick him up.

After his release, he sought asylum in the US. Even thousands of miles away he still feels the government's pinch. He says: "After I came to America in October 2012, I was contacted by Chinese police of Xiamen University, who told me I published some 'inappropriate words' on the internet and asked me when I would go back to China

and invited me to 'drink tea' with him at the police station. You know what he meant, that equals an interrogation by the police."

On top of torture and imprisonments, other lawyers say they have been seized while trying to meet clients. Others are repeatedly refused access to detainees and to case material. These are the most extreme manifestations of the crackdown. More commonplace tactics include refusal to renew legal licenses, which happens annually in order for lawyers to continue practicing.

It's this tactic that Liang Xiaojong has become familiar with. Since 2009, Liang has worked at the Beijing Dao Heng law firm. He deals with a large number of high-profile cases, including ones concerning Re-Education Through Labour, a controversial system of detention centres, and Falun Gong. He

# Five to six years ago, they targeted only a very small number of lawyers, but now dozens have been affected

says that it's the local public security organs who give him "the greatest obstacles". They recently notified the Beijing Bureau of Justice about the highly sensitive cases he has taken on, who in turn "warned him off" taking more sensitive cases.

Part of the issue is that Chinese human rights lawyers are prolific on social media and are becoming more outspoken. They attempt to harness public opinion and encourage debate about cases. Often these cases are ones with a large majority of public support. This working style, combined with a combative approach and less fear of authority, has led to them being labelled *sike* – "diehard" lawyers.

The government sees human rights lawyers as a threat. Support for rule-of-law reforms has become far more open in China. Today human rights lawyers are banding  →

→ together to support each other. Often now, when lawyers are arrested, people take to the Chinese social media network Weibo to challenge the system. This unnerves the country's leaders who fear, above all, an increasingly assertive civil society will threaten their legitimacy.

"Superficially, Xi's Party and government are clamping down on lawyers and dissidents more severely than in the past. It is, in fact, because more lawyers and dissidents dare to challenge communist rule now," says Jin.

Wang agrees, adding that human rights lawyers have moved from the margins closer to the mainstream and that has provoked the government's shift in tactic. The government is now going after those who demand moderate rather than radical change.

"Human rights lawyers in the past were able to do quite a lot of things without too much harassment, but then they became more vocal, took on more cases of a sensitive nature and pushed boundaries."

However, these acts of reprisal have galvanised China's community of lawyers. Some law firms have been intimidated into not hiring human rights lawyers, but others are undeterred. Liang, for one, continues to practice this type of law, having not been explicitly told to stop. And according to Amnesty's 2013 annual review, released this year in March, a wave of new lawyers have joined the profession.

In response to the frequent threats and assaults, hundreds have also banded together under the name China Human Rights Lawyers Group. They released open letters and statements calling for an end to rights violations targeting these lawyers. For example, more than 40 lawyers jointly signed a "Letter of Intent for Mutual Support Among Chinese Lawyers" in April 2014. Its purpose was to ensure strength through numbers, so that anyone who is oppressed can expect help from their peers.

"China is a victim of its own success," Nee says. "This is not to say that the government is the bad guy uniformly, just that society is becoming too diverse for government to use the same tactics as in the past."

Perhaps then China is changing for the better. Optimists might argue it's a case of one step back, two steps forward. As for Jin he is taking no chances. His ambition, as he sees it, is to "build China into a country of rule of law and guarantee its people's freedom and basic human rights by a constitutional government". But he accepts that for now he has to do this from afar. X

© Jemimah Steinfeld
www.indexoncensorship.org

**Jemimah Steinfeld** is a contributing editor to Index on Censorship and is the author of upcoming book Little Emperors and Material Girls: Sex and Youth in Modern China. She tweets @JFSteinfeld

# Taking down the critics

43(3): 79/82 | DOI: 10.1177/0306422014548146

The Ecuadorian government is accused of using a Spanish legal firm to employ copyright laws and get critical posts removed from Twitter, Facebook and YouTube. **Irene Caselli** reports

**D**IANA AMORES IS not what you would call a high-profile Twitter user. With around 3,000 followers, her tweets mix political commentary with personal messages, jokes and replies to insults.

The 34-year-old Ecuadorean translator signed up to the social network in 2011 to join an online campaign against the government's plans to allow mining in an environmentally sensitive area. Little did she know that some of her sarcastic political tweets would eventually get her into trouble.

In early 2014, Spanish law firm Ares Rights contacted Twitter to demand it removed content from Amores's account for infringing copyright laws. The firm appears to have been acting on behalf of Ecuador's governing party.

As a result, the account, @diana_amores, was temporarily suspended. Amores was surprised, but also outraged: she appealed and her account was soon activated again. "I am not a hero, but I was not going to stay quiet," she told Index on Censorship. "This was a clear abuse of the copyright law."

Amores is one of many internet users who have been targeted by Ares Rights, which contacts websites insisting content is taken down under a US law, the Digital Millennium Copyright Act (DMCA). The firm has asked for documentaries, tweets and search results to be removed from the web, saying they are infringing copyright.

The DMCA, approved by the US Congress in 1998, was designed to modernise copyright law for the internet era. The act allows for takedown requests to be sent to websites publishing material that infringes copyright. Most sites receiving takedown requests react by automatically removing content to avoid any legal problems. If uploaders file a successful counter-notice, as Amores did, the material can be put back online.

In theory DMCA notices are a quick and hassle-free way to protect copyright – but in practice they can be misused.

"In the wrong hands, the DMCA can be used for temporary censorship," says Adam Holland, a project coordinator at Harvard University's Berkman Center for Internet and Society. Holland also works with the Chilling Effect database, an online archive started in 2001 to keep track of takedown notices. Chilling Effect researches how DMCA notices are being used to censor material.

Big companies such as Google, YouTube and Twitter receive huge numbers of notices every day. Twitter gets about 1,000 per month, Google close to seven million. Holland argues that the incentive to verify whether all those notices are legitimate is small. Firms such as Ares Rights have →

ABOVE: Ecuador's president, Rafael Correa, awaits a press conference. Correa has successfully pursued several libel lawsuits against the media

Credit: DPA Picture Alliance / Alamy

→  many clients who are willing to pay them to monitor internet activity and send notices.

In Ecuador, Ares Rights is alleged to have acted on behalf of the Alianza PAIS governing party, EcuadorTV (the state-run television station) and even President Rafael Correa.

Since coming into power in 2007, Correa has attracted international criticism for his treatment of media. He has been accused of double standards – granting Wikileaks founder Julian Assange asylum in the Ecuadorean embassy in London but clamping down on freedom of speech at home.

Correa has successfully pursued several lawsuits against local private media for libel and regularly insults reporters, calling them *bestias salvajes* and *sicarios de tinta* ("wild beasts" and "ink hitmen"). He regularly insists, in his weekly Citizen Link television show, that he is fighting against powerful elites with strong economic interests, who have traditionally been represented by private media in Ecuador.

In 2013, the National Assembly approved a communications law, which created a state watchdog to regulate newspaper and television content. The government said this was a step toward more balanced media. "The law is there to create a good press, good information, true freedom of expression, to make sure that the corrupt press doesn't make up something new every day – that is lying and manipulating," explained Correa in one of his weekly addresses. Journalists said it was a blow to free speech. Two media outlets were sued for their coverage of a trip Correa made to Chile and a cartoonist was ordered to modify the text on his image. Other aspects of the law have been praised. For example, the law fairly distributes broadcast frequencies: 34% to state broadcasters, 33% to private media and 33% to community broadcasting, thus allowing for what many consider media pluralism.

Many Ecuadorian editors have said that self-censorship has become one of the main results of the new law. On World Press Freedom Day, 3 May, media outlets abstained from republishing an illustration created by the World Association of Newspapers and News Publishers criticising Correa for his stance against the media. Ecuadorean editors published only images created by the association related to China and Ethiopia.

According to Chilling Effect, Ares Rights has been active since 2010. Last year, the company sent a DMCA notice to get confidential documents removed from online library Scribd.com, the online library. The documents had been posted by a reporter from Buzzfeed.com, who had revealed that the Ecuadorean government had purchased equipment to carry out large-scale domestic surveillance. Although the ministry of the interior said the documents were fake, Ares Rights sent DMCA notices. Once the documents were taken off Scribd and uploaded on Dropbox, Ares Rights sent a new notification. Buzzfeed sent a counter-notice, and the files were put back online.

Ares Rights also successfully removed an anti-mining video by Ecuadorean filmmaker Pocho Álvarez, Acoso a Intag (Intimidation in Intag), which showed Correa's insults – broadcast on national television – against the people of Intag, a town that fought against mining in its biodiverse area, as well as an anti-government short film called Cómo

Miente el Presidente de la República (How the President of the Republic Lies). Another critical documentary, Rafael Correa: Retrato de un Padre de la Patria (Rafael Correa: Portrait of a Father of the Motherland), by Colombian filmmaker Santiago Villa, was also taken down from YouTube. Acoso a Intag and Rafael Correa: Retrato de un Padre de la Patria were later reinstated.

Claiming to be acting on behalf of Correa, Ares Rights sent a notice to Twitter regarding a posted picture where Correa is seen next to a woman during a party. The notice says the takedown is "extremely urgent", because it concerns "distribution of images of the private sphere of our client".

# Twitter gets about 1,000 takedown requests per month from around the world; Google gets close to seven million

Ares Rights is based in Barcelona, but few details are available about its work. The company's website links to Twitter and Facebook profiles with little activity and few followers. There is a Vimeo video posted on its main page. "Piracy control in real time," says the video. "Transparent, clean, fast, safe, without lawsuits, simple strategy to monitor websites."

During an investigative series for Ecuador's El Universo newspaper, journalist Mónica Almeida tried to contact the company but found none of the company's registered details led anywhere. Index on Censorship also tried to contact the company via social networks but received no reply. In its transparency report about the firm, Google states: "We believe it is an impostor or someone who is abusing the process. We report this action here to guarantee completeness and show one of the types of abuse of the DMCA process." Google, which owns YouTube, told Index that it is working $\rightarrow$

→ "to detect and reject invalid takedown requests", adding that the work done by NGOs and the media is currently hugely beneficial for informing on the misuse of copyright claims.

Amores first received a DMCA notice in 2013 on her YouTube channel, where she had uploaded a copy of an anti-mining video by Ecuadorean filmmaker Pocho Álvarez. She paid little attention to these notices, as the video was available on several other sites.

In February 2014, as Ecuadoreans geared up for municipal elections, Amores posted a collage of pictures of local candidates with President Correa, who had previously said he was "happily not running for any post". In her sarcastic tweet, Amores said: "Hmm... Who is this guy who appears in all these pictures?" In another post, Amores reproduced the electoral publicity of another local candidate.

She received takedown notices for both tweets. They were sent by Ares Rights on behalf of Movimiento Alianza PAIS, Ecuador's government party. She appealed and her tweets were put back online. But Ares Rights sent a new notice a month later for using the image of another politician, Fernando Cordero, former president of the National Assembly and former head of the country's pensions system. A fourth notice arrived in connection to her republishing an open letter by Correa.

After this fourth notice, her account was suspended. Amores created a new account, reported what had happened on the social network and appealed. It took 24 hours until her account was reactivated.

Twitter also took down another image she had posted poking fun at the president's weekly Saturday address. The copyright claim was over the official government logo that was used with a video still from the Simpsons cartoon show. This time Ares Rights filed a complaint on behalf of EcuadorTV, the state TV channel that broadcasts the show. She never received a notice for this takedown, so the image remains blocked. Index asked Twitter to comment but received no reply.

After leaving his position as CEO for Ecuador's state broadcaster in April 2014, Enrique Arosemena denied any relation with Ares Rights. "To be very clear, EcuadorTV has no relation with Ares Rights. It has signed no contract." Mónica Almeida of El Universo tried to contact several government officials but received no answer. Index on Censorship also asked Ecuador's national secretary of communications, Fernando Alvarado, for an interview. Alvarado is in charge of the government's communications strategy, as well as all national broadcasters, and is one of the main advisers to the president. In an email, Alvarado's press secretary, Mariana Bravo, said: "The national secretary of communications expresses his thanks for the request, but is not interested in the interview."

"The situation is very critical," says Cesar Ricaurte, director of the Ecuadorean NGO Fundamedios. Ricaurte says that since the law was approved, two printed publications have shut down, there have been more than 100 proceedings against media and more than 30 prosecutions, including one against a cartoonist. "Facing the closing down of spaces for expression within traditional media, social networks acquire a growing importance in Ecuador," says Ricaurte.

Amores agrees. She was once a supporter of Correa: in 2006, she voted for him, thinking he might be able to bring about significant change. But now she believes it was a mistake. "Social networks have become the last bastion of true freedom of expression in Ecuador," she says. "I have few followers and my account has little impact. How uneasy does the government feel about criticism if they go after people like me?" ☒

@ Irene Caselli
www.indexoncensorship.org

**Irene Caselli** is a multimedia journalist working in Latin America. She covered Ecuador for BBC News and others from 2009 to 2013. She is now based in Argentina

# Maid equal in Brazil

43(3): 83/86 | DOI: 10.1177/0306422014548626

A Twitter feed is exposing how millions of Brazilian domestic workers are treated as an underclass. **Claire Rigby** reports from São Paulo

**"M**Y IDIOT MAID waits till I have dirtied five blouses, then washes them all at once. She's an imbecile." "I asked the maid where my tablet was and she pointed to the Kindle, the ignorant creature." "I hate it when my maid cleans the living room. She always unplugs the wi-fi, the whore."

Delving into the timeline of Brazilian Twitter account @aminhaempregada is a sobering experience, like eavesdropping on hundreds of conversations taking place in every far-flung corner of the country. The account was created in May to aggregate and retweet posts using the term *a minha empregada* ("my maid") or the word *empregada* ("maid").

"That idiot", "that slut", "the lazy whore" are some of the choice phrases that show up alongside the words *minha empregada*. Another favourite is *filha da puta* ("daughter of a whore") or – because on Twitter, every character counts – more often just *fdp*.

"I think the most offensive tweets are the racist ones," says the account's creator and curator, a young marketing professional who prefers to remain anonymous. "I remember one that said something like, 'My maid was supposed to wash my trainers and she hasn't done it, the dirty *macaca*' ['monkey', a racist insult]. Some people feel at extraordinary liberty to speak freely on the internet."

On Twitter, with its relatively elite group of users, there's no *a minha patroa* ("my boss") equivalent so the other side of the story can be heard, and very few posts by domestic workers themselves in response to @aminhaempregada. Some children of maids reply. "My mother is a maid, but they treat her so well I never imagined there were people who disrespected maids like this," wrote one of @aminhaempregada's thousands of followers. A male domestic worker wrote: "I'm north-eastern, black, a domestic worker and poor. No one knows how we suffer." His voice is the exception.

## He explains how in Brazil even the terms "my maid" is loaded and that gave him the idea of searching Twitter for it

Type *empregada doméstica* into a search engine and the results are mainly agencies or information on employers' responsibilities. That lack of a public voice mirrors maids' social isolation in the workplace, especially for live-in employees. There are thought to be some nine million domestic employees working in the country currently, and the man behind @aminhaempregada, like millions Brazilians of even slightly affluent means, was raised by a succession of maids himself. "I loved our maids," he tells Index. "I still have the vinyl record one of them gave me for my birthday when I was a →

ABOVE: Maids take a break on Copacabana beach in Rio de Janeiro, Brazil

but the phrase 'my maid' had always made me feel uncomfortable when I hear it."

The term has a proprietorial ring to it: domestic service is a sensitive subject in Brazil, where the scars of slavery still run deep. According to the Trans-Atlantic Slave Trade Database, 4.86 million African slaves were shipped to Brazil from the mid-1500s until the late 1800s, compared to 388,000 shipped directly to North America.

A constitutional amendment was passed in March 2013 to establish a range of rights for domestic employees, including the right to an eight-hour day, extra pay for overtime and nights, and basic health and safety guarantees. The amendment, presented by Benedita da Silva, a member of Congress and a former domestic servant herself, is expected to be consolidated this year with a second raft of legislation dealing with some of the thornier nitty-gritty needed to bring the rights of domestic employees into line with those of the rest of Brazilian workers. There is currently a debate in Congress over whether the employers of domestic workers will have to shoulder the same financial responsibilities, when firing their employees, as companies.

Carlos Alberto Pinto de Carvalho is an employment lawyer and a partner in the start-up Webhome, a website providing legal advice for domestic employers. He supports the legislation and its effect of formalising the relationship between maids and their employers. "It mainly serves to guarantee payment for overtime and nights," he says. "But it also sends a message to employers that they run the risk of being fined and empowers employees to speak up for themselves."

A lack of reliable information, however, means that the ability to speak up is complicated for domestic employees, many of whom have limited education and lack the resources to find out about new rights and legislation.

"A friend of mine told me about the new law for domestic workers," says Valdenes

→ child. It's one of my treasured possessions." Still shocked daily by the tweets that show up in his search feeds, he explains how in Brazil even the term "my maid" is loaded

## Domestic service is a sensitive subject in Brazil, where the scars of slavery still run deep

and that was what gave him the idea of searching Twitter for it.

"The term is not technically wrong – of course people say 'my doctor', 'my dentist',

Lopes de Oliveira, 43, who has worked as a maid since she was 17. "She saw something about it on the daytime news."

Does she think the government has a duty to find ways to divulge the information about domestic employees' new rights?

"I think the press does," she says. "I am only able to watch the news in the evening, and I've never seen it reported there at all. They should report it more, so everyone can see it."

As a result of her friend's information, Lopes informed her employer that she was now legally entitled to a lunch break.

"She said I could have 15 minutes for a sandwich, but I told her I need at least 30 minutes. I need a proper meal at lunchtime," says Lopes. A cooked lunch underpinned by rice and beans is a non-negotiable part of the day for most Brazilian workers. "I don't know how long we're allowed by law," Lopes continues. "Could you find out and let me know?"

The law, says Pinto de Carvalho, allows for an hour's break for lunch in an eight-hour working day. "My sister says, 'Why don't you train to be a hairdresser?'" says Lopes. "But I like the job – I like the people I work for." For a younger generation of women who might previously have gone into the profession, rising affluence and initiatives like the government's *Bolsa Familia* programme, which distributes cash benefits to millions of families on low incomes, has created new opportunities.

"Nobody wants to be a maid anymore," says Lopes. One friend of hers has left the profession to study to become a teacher, and many of the other younger women she knows are busy pursuing careers and studies in areas like IT, hairdressing and nursing.

Meanwhile, for thousands of families accustomed to having their every need met by a servant, the prospect of having to do their own housework looms. A headline in a recent feature in Bonde, a Brazilian news and entertainment website, is a harbinger of the changes afoot: "No maid? Read on to find out how to keep your home clean and tidy yourself." ☒

© Claire Rigby
www.indexoncensorship.org

**Claire Rigby** is a freelance journalist based in Brazil. She is a co-founder of Fluxo, an experimental journalism studio in downtown São Paulo

||||||||||||||||||||||||||||||||||||||||||||||||||||||||||||||||||||||||||||||||||||||||||||||||||||||||||||||

# Home truths in the Gulf

.........................................................

*The United Arab Emirates is increasing rights for domestic workers, but many are still afraid to speak about employer abuse and failure to pay wages, writes* **Georgia Lewis**

Bosede and Deka, two African maids working in the United Arab Emirates, have been trapped in limbo for the past three years, after their employers confiscated their passports and refused to pay them for work. Left without the ability to get legal employment, they went to their embassy for help. There they were told they could only have replacement documents if they purchased air tickets home first. Given that they do not have the money to do this, Bosede and Deke remain in the UAE, picking up cash-in-hand work, and still without passports. They claim their wages have not been paid.

Maids in the UAE are afraid to speak out about the conditions they face because of the threats to their visa status, or because they are working illegally. Labour laws are hard to implement and do not cover domestic workers. The absence of an income tax system also makes it hard to keep track of who is working and where. However, a new unified contract for domestic staff, introduced in June, may make a difference. The aim is to give maids hired by recruitment agencies protection from abuse, and employers protection from financial loss.

Michael Barney, director of Gulf Law, a law firm that works with Filipino expats in the UAE, says: "When the rules are clearer, maids will know their rights and can demand their employers observe these rules. It is really more about informing the maids of what their employers can and cannot do." The new law guarantees regular payments, a weekly day off with full pay, 14 days' paid annual leave and sick leave of up to 30 days. But Barney also recognises that many maids have entered the UAE undocumented, often "buying" a visa so they can work freelance or working cash-in-hand.

Official figures from the 2009 census show 321,536 women working in domestic jobs in the country, 80 per cent of them earning less than Dh1,300 (around US$350) per month. Often stories of abused maids only come to light in the UAE media when cases end up in court. Cases of rape that result in pregnancy may end up coming to the public's attention as adultery cases in breach of sharia law, which outlaws all extramarital sex. It is also common for agreements to be reached at the end of trials that prohibit victims from speaking publicly.

While reporting on maids has not been widespread in the region's media in the past, their stories are now getting more coverage, according to Barney. He says many cases involving abuse of domestic workers have become "quite high-profile", including a life sentence in March for a Pakistani man convicted of raping a Filipina maid in Dubai and seven-year sentences in February for two Emirati men convicted of raping a Filipina maid in Fujairah. "Before, stories like these were not really of major interest so they were not highly publicised. Now that more people are showing concern over the issue, the media are highlighting them."

The media landscape in UAE is also broadening. There is now a UAE-based Filipino radio station, TAG 91.1, which launched in March 2013, as well two weekly print-and-online newspapers, The Filipino Times, which launched in October 2013, and Kabayan Weekly, which launched in 2011. X

© Georgia Lewis
www.indexoncensorship.org

*Some names have been changed*

**Georgia Lewis** is a London-based journalist, originally from Australia, who spent five years working in Dubai and Abu Dhabi

# Text messaging

43(3): 87/90 | DOI: 10.1177/0306422014548661

The new Indian government has signalled that it wants schoolbooks edited in line with Hindu religious beliefs, reports **Siddharth Narrain**

SCHOOL AND COLLEGE textbooks, and their editors, are at the centre of an important freedom of expression battle with religious power in India. The newly elected Hindu nationalist BJP-led National Democratic Alliance (NDA) government flagged the textbooks issue just weeks after the election when the minister for human resources development, Smriti Irani, in one of her first speeches, announced that the government would "Hinduise" the content of textbooks. Irani is not alone in the project.

The Rashtriya Swayamsevak Sangh, an organisation that represents the cultural and social agenda of the ruling BJP and its affiliate organisations, such as the Shiksha Bachao Andolan Samiti (Save Education Struggle Committee), headed by the indomitable Deena Nath Batra, have been fighting for years to remove any references in curriculums that they perceive as "hurting" Hindu sentiments, or portraying Hindus in bad light. Batra has been in the media spotlight for targeting a number of highly rated academic works, including Wendy Doniger's books The Hindus: An Alternative History and On Hinduism. She also attacked Sekhar Bandopadhayay's From Plassey to Partition: A History of Modern India.

The controversy over textbooks in India is similar to the attempts in Texas in the US to change school curriculums to reflect conservative values. Republicans on school boards have systematically targeted science and history textbooks to reflect "family values" and support creationism, despite the objections of scientists.

In a move, reminiscent of the debates in Texas, the Gujarat government has issued a circular recommending six books written by Batra should be used for primary and secondary school students. Local newspapers have pointed out that Batra's books speak of an undivided India (Akhand Bharat), a definition that includes neighbouring countries and fits into an expansionist Hindu nationalist view of the world. In these books, Batra advises against blowing out birthday candles, suggesting this is a Western cultural practice to be avoided. The Shiksha Bachao Andolan Samiti has also objected to academic material that it deems critical of Hinduism saying that it "hurts the sentiments of Hindus".

The battle over textbooks is not new: in the early 1990s, the then NDA government initiated a process of "saffronisation" of school curriculums, an attempt by Hindu right-wing thinkers to influence education curriculums. This trend was reversed over the last decade when the United Progressive Alliance was in power. But Irani's recent statements may be the beginnings of a new battle. There is an overlap here between the demands of the Shiksha Bachao Andolan Samiti and the government's own ideological leanings. Both believe that current curriculums need to develop education according to "Indian ideals and →

ABOVE: Children study textbooks at a school in rural Rajasthan, northern India

→ values". The emphasis here is on moral conservatism and on India's Hindu heritage. They want curriculums to have a historical slant towards revisionist interpretations that

## The government announced that it would "Hinduise" the content of textbooks

show Muslim rulers and Islamic tradition in a negative light, and Hindu rulers and traditions in a positive light, even if this means eliding the pernicious impact of caste or gender hierarchies.

Claims of "hurt religious sentiment" have emerged in recent years, often linked to the threat to public order. For instance, Wendy Doniger was accused of sexualising the portrayal of the Hindu religion. The other argument is that the content of school curriculums is too secular and ignores "indigenous" Indian, ie Hindu, streams of knowledge.

For those advocating a more liberal legal framework the deluge of legal claims around "hurt sentiments" has become a troublesome feature of the manner in which the Indian law has worked to limit speech. Examples of groups that have made these claims in the recent past include religious groups (Hindus, Muslims, Christians), caste groups

(Lingayats, Dalits), occupation-based groups, which have strong caste associations (washer men, cobblers), and language groups (Oriya speakers). In a number of editorials in newspapers and magazines, India is now referred to as a "Republic of Hurt Sentiments".

Successive Indian governments have responded to criticism of the law by citing the history of communal disturbances in the country, and conflict based on caste, religion, ethnicity and language, but the fact is they have chosen to regulate speech rather than provide protection to those speaking and expressing their views.

The courts in India have become an important battleground. For instance, in the Doniger case: after a two-year legal battle Doniger's publishers, Penguin, came to an informal agreement with the petitioners, Shiksha Bachao Andolan Samiti. Penguin agreed to pulp recalled, unsold and withdrawn copies at its own cost, sparking international widespread outrage. Penguin, while defending their actions, has cited the Indian legal framework as one of the reasons for their action. The problem with the Indian legal framework, though, is not the law in itself.

The substantive law around "hurt sentiments" is situated mostly in three provisions of the Indian Penal Code; 153a (promoting enmity between different groups on grounds of religion, race, etc), 295a (deliberate and malicious acts intended to outrage religious feelings) and 298 (uttering words with deliberate intent to wound religious feelings).

Indian courts have held that the manner of discourse and nature and text of captions is significant. This can be illustrated by a case decided by the Supreme Court in 1980, concerning articles written by Babu Rao Patel. The court dealt with an allegation under section 153a related to two articles, A Tale of Two Communalisms and Lingering Disgrace of History in a magazine called Mother India. The petitioner was convicted under section 153a by the trial court, and the conviction was confirmed by the Sessions Court and the Delhi High Court. Babu Rao Patel claimed that A Tale of Two Communalisms was a political thesis and that Lingering Disgrace of History was based on historical truths against the naming of roads in Delhi after Mughal emperors. The court analysed both the articles. It said that the first article began as a political thesis but degenerated into hate speech. For instance, the author referred to Muslims generally as "a basically violent race" and alleged that communalism in India was an instrument of a minority with a racial tradition of rape, loot, violence and murder. The author proposed that the only solution to communalism was to declare India a Hindu State. The court said that this clearly amounted to hate speech, and was undisguised attempt to promote feelings of enmity and hatred between the Hindu and Muslim communities.

# In a number of editorials, India is now referred to as a "Republic of Hurt Sentiments"

The court held that the second article dealt with much more than just the naming of Delhi's road after Mughal emperors. Among the reasons that the authors argued that Delhi's roads should be renamed were "the endless raids, rapes, loot, arson and slaughter" perpetuated by Muslims. In the article the author said, "To have a street named after this Mughal bastard in New Delhi, the capital of India, is not only a disgrace to the Hindus but a crying insult to the brave community of Sikhs." The court held that it was wrong for the author to vilify Muslims, and to promote feelings of enmity, hatred and ill will between the Hindu and Muslim communities. The judgement said this could not be done under the guise of political thesis or historical truth.

Judges have recognised the freedom to express diverse viewpoints and freedom →

→ of creativity and art as long as the mode of delivery and the language used does not indicate a deliberate and malicious intention to hurt sentiments or outrage feelings.

Courts have also consistently held that academic material is highly protected unless the language used is crude or coarse. For example, the Bombay High Court decision, in 1982, where the Maharashtra state government forfeited copies of the Marathi weekly Shree for violating section 153a. The government argued that the article's attempts to show that Arabian culture in pre-Islamic times were influenced by Indian culture would promote disharmony between Muslim and Hindu communities. The petitioners argued successfully that the author was a well-known research scholar and that the article was based on historical evidence,

## At stake is not just the right to have access to information, but the way future generations view the world

dealing with the religious, cultural and socio-historical background in west Asia before the advent of Islam.

The court held that while truthful and historical accounts are not completely exempt from the purview of 153a, scholarly articles stood on a different footing. The court said that it would be very difficult for it to hold that the narration of history could promote violence, enmity or hatred. The court said:

*If such a contention is accepted, a day will come when that part of history which is unpalatable to a particular religion will have to be kept in cold storage on the pretext that the publication of such history would constitute an offence punishable under Section 153a of the IPC. We do not think that the scope of Section*

*153a can be enlarged to such an extent with a view to thwart history. For obvious reasons, history and historical events cannot be allowed to be looked as a secret on a specious plea that if the history is made known to a person who is interested to know the history, there is likelihood of someone else being hurt.*

Ironically, the trend in India today has been for academic publishers to capitulate, instead of fighting their cases through the courts. The problem for publishers, and those at the receiving end of "hurt sentiment" claims, is that once courts agree to take on these cases, the time, money and effort that goes into fighting them within the legal system, is a form of punishment itself. An effective strategy for Batra and others has been to file these claims in small towns, where lower courts admit these matters. The accused is then summoned across the country, causing much inconvenience. This is possible because the cause of action can be the place of production, circulation or distribution of the offending material.

Initiatives to change the content of school textbooks, and to prevent the publication of academic material on the grounds of "hurt sentiment", make this issue a serious threat to free expression. At stake is not just the right to have access to information, but the way future generations view the world. The courts have become an important site for this battle, and the arsenal of existing penal provisions are the weapons increasingly being brandished to enforce the writ of the religious right. This trend can only be stopped through a mobilisation of liberal voices, and by making sure that none of these changes happen without a fight. ☒

© Siddharth Narrain
www.indexoncensorship.org

**Siddharth Narrain** is a legal researcher and lawyer with the Alternative Law Forum, Bangalore

# We have to fight for what we want

43(3): 91/94 | DOI: 10.1177/0306422014548977

Dunja Mijatović has spent more than 20 years as a champion of free speech – and is now an official advocate. Index editor **Rachael Jolley** talks to her about attacks on journalists and the need for trust in news

**T**HREATS TO THE public's access right to information never go away. One person charged with bringing those threats to our attention is Dunja Mijatović, the Organisation for Security and Cooperation in Europe (OSCE) representative on freedom of the media. She is concerned, and a little down-hearted, that societies appear to have learned so little from history when it comes to defending the right for the media to criticise governments, to provide different points of view or to bring information to the public's ears.

All over the world it feels as if the right to argue, discuss and disagree is not valued as highly as it has been in the past. The exceptions are few, but Germany, especially among those old enough to remember the pre-1989 era, is one of them. Others are those European nations in Europe where people have never really seen sign of the democracy that the post-Wall euphoria promised. In Belarus and Azerbaijan, the fight for a free media has never gone away. In other nations, a self-satisfied lack of concern has settled in. But Mijatović is having none of it.

With Russia and Ukraine standing eyeball to eyeball and an military offensive in Gaza covered live on daily television news bulletins, good journalism has never been more

vital. Milatović, who leads the Vienna-based OSCE unit specialising in media freedom and freedom of expression, is watching closely as nations pick up propaganda tools not only to control the message, but to create it; while at the same time trying to restrict the number of channels that the public can use to find out what is really going on. Trusted news sources are often in short supply, with news agencies and TV stations under financial pressure and journalists being attacked.

The organisation she works for, the OSCE, has 57 member nations and around 2,600 staff, and despite its name, members from three continents, Europe, Asia and North America. Its mission is to work with its member states, from Russia to the US, Turkey and the Ukraine, to protect economic, political and individual security. It works with states and groups within them to create and sustain democracy, to prevent conflict and to offer mediation. The majority of its staff work in the field, rather than at its main offices. OSCE staff were some of the first international observers in Ukraine after the Malaysian Airlines crash. As media freedom improves or slides in the other direction, Mijatović is there to report on it.

Mijatović grew up in Sarajevo and attended the city's university. After the Yugoslavian →

ABOVE: Dunja Mijatović, OSCE representative on freedom of the media, in Vienna in January

→ war she was one of the founders of the Communications Regulatory Agency of Bosnia and Herzegovina, a media regulator, so it is natural that Mijatović keeps a careful eye on the region. Right now, she is not impressed by what she sees. There was a period of massive improvement: better legislation, promoting safety of journalists, fighting impunity and decriminalising defamation. But now she has identified a backward slide in the countries of the former Yugoslavia and in Albania. "There is a huge decline in media freedoms in the region, after a very long period, almost 20 years of struggle." The European Commission can exert pressure on those countries, because they wish to join the EU and need to meet criteria to quality. So she has suggested to the EU that it needs to step in and do so. "They are the only ones with a stick… This negative trend needs to be reversed immediately. If not, we are going to be in a big trouble," she says. "What we have now is politics again trying to interfere, put pressure and control media in a very blunt and open way." She appears blunt and open, though she also has highly developed political antennae.

As the 25th anniversary of the fall of the Berlin Wall approaches, it is appropriate to review the optimism of 1989, and the belief that a wider, greater democracy was on its way. Mijatović says that optimism was justified, but the problem was that no one did enough to protect the hard-fought-for freedoms. She feels that society at large is far too blasé about freedom. Her office is in Vienna, just an hour away by road from the border of Belarus, where journalists find themselves under house arrest for publishing criticism of the government. But she worries that most people in Western countries don't even think about that. Sometimes we take freedoms for granted, particularly in democracies and free countries, and we forget how it is when those freedoms are suppressed. "I think if we have censorship in Belarus, which is just around the corner, that also affects societies living in freedom at the same time, and much more needs to be done."

While she spends much of her time fighting for journalists, she is not going to shy away from criticising them either. "There's a lack of solidarity. Many journalists could do more to protect the dignity of their profession." She would like to see journalists coming together to fight for their professional values, rather than attacking each other's politics. She is holding meetings with Russian and Ukrainian journalists to try and get them to discuss protecting journalism. The OSCE also works all the time with the profession, and is currently holding a series of workshops on "open journalism" and its implications, attempting to help and advise on how citizens who now write and report, but have not had any formal trained, are fully informed of legal risks and protections of how they work. She wants representatives of the 57 states to listen to stories and problems that "citizen journalists" are facing. The new world of reporting has not prepared those who are doing the work for the obstacles they might face.

Use of propaganda is, of course, nothing new, but the way it is being used, particularly in Ukraine and Russia, has attracted attention from her office. Mijatović has first-hand knowledge of the impact of propaganda during the Yugoslav war. "It was mainly Milošević's regime that was using propaganda as a tool to inject hatred amongst people, to divide people, but there was no internet at that time. Now with the internet, we've moved to another level."

The mix of propaganda and censorship is in the ascendancy in Russia. Vladimir Putin's government has placed new controls on private media, the ones most likely to carry stories critical of its actions. Under a recent proposal passed by Russia's Duma, only TV stations that fulfil certain criteria will be allowed to carry advertising. Experts suggest this could lead to the closure of up to 150 stations. This move has the power to

## Sometimes we take freedoms for granted, particularly in democracies. We forget how it is when liberty is suppressed

shut down the voices of hundreds of regional broadcasters, says Mijatović. As if Russian media were not already constrained enough, severe restrictions on income will force journalists and editors to think long and hard about running any story that threatens their business's ability to survive.

Mijatović, an enthusiastic user of social media, has her eye on the rising use of technology as a tool of censorship as well as propaganda. Her un-ending battle is to persuade states that a future with more openness and more voices competing to be heard is better for them and better for their citizens. Many might find that a depressing role right now. "I try to raise the importance of fighting propaganda, not with blocking and filtering and breaching of channels but with more voices and pluralism and reform of these old state broadcasters – which →

→ were not reformed for so many years – and offering balanced, fair and impartial views. Of course this cannot solve the problems overnight in a post-Soviet country or in the Balkans. But I don't see any other way of fighting propaganda." She also says that Ukrainian authorities also are pushing to control broadcasters. "I don't think this a solution to the problem, because you cannot stop the signals, satellite, internet. So much more needs to be done in order to fight propaganda but this sort of hasty attempt to stop voices, no matter how ridiculous these voices are, is not going to help in my view."

She has also spoken out about the EU "right to be forgotten" ruling, worried that it will increase self-censorship by intermediaries such as Google and that it will infringe upon the public's ability to find out legitimate information. Also on her agenda is preserving net neutrality. "In the Western countries, the European Union countries, there are more and more cases that are extraordinary for democracies. In the US, I raised several cases in relation to the protection of sources and net neutrality, so it is very difficult to think about one country and say this is really is a bad guy."

When it comes to sorting out the world's attitudes to freedom of speech her answer is more education. "I do not think that governments are putting in enough funds and efforts in order to offer more literacy when we talk about media. And not to mention internet literacy nowadays – that should start in kindergarten. Governments would rather put funds into blocking and filtering, because they think that will solve all the problems in society."

She is also aware of rising levels of pressure on journalists not to publish critical stories about those in power, not only in member-states of the OSCE. "What we see is that there is more and more intimidation. There are attempts to stop critical voices, provocative voices, adoption of new laws overnight, everything in the name of security, the fight against terrorism, protection of minors, all possible ways that are in a way legitimate ways of any government to protect society and its citizens but if you look at the cases that are popping out in certain countries after the adoption of those laws, you can see that they are used for everything else than actually protecting citizens."

Mijatović, who is clearly tireless, believes strongly that we have to get better at accepting that criticism is a healthy part of life. Right now across Europe and beyond, her message appears to be falling on deaf ears. X

© Rachael Jolley
www.indexoncensorship.org

**Rachael Jolley** is the editor of Index on Censorship magazine. She tweets @london-insider. Follow the magazine on Twitter @index_magazine

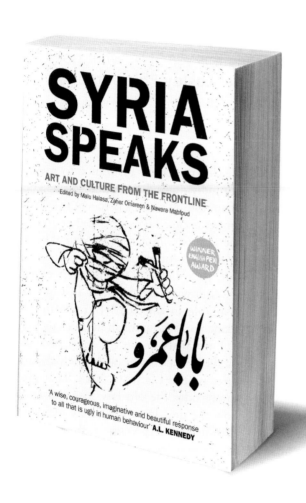

# Decoding defamation

43(3): 96/100 | DOI: 10.1177/0306422014548150

UK defamation law was reformed early this year, but what does it mean for the media? Journalism lecturer **Lesley Phippen** offers a need-to-know guide on the changes

**Y**OUNG JOURNALISTS AND who aspire to enter the trade are too often unaware of the legal risks they face. Understanding defamation law is a vital part of being a reporter.

Journalists want to publish interesting and important stories. To do this, they often have to include information that individuals or companies dislike because it casts them in a bad light. The threat of a defamation action has often been used to stifle unwanted publicity even when the information is true. Accuracy and facts are essential. Journalists need to know how to present information. Are they detailing a fact or expressing an opinion? If a story is published that turns out to be incorrect, is the story in the public interest? Knowledge of all this is required in order to avoid a defamation action.

Even if you are prepared to fight your corner and believe that your story is true, the cost of defending it can be high. When Simon Singh was sued by the British Chiropractic Association (BCA) he spent more than £200,000 before the Court of Appeal ruled that he could use the old common law defence of fair comment and the action was dropped. Singh had criticised the BCA about the way in which certain treatments were publicised or promoted by them. He expressed his views in The Guardian, but the BCA decided to sue Singh personally.

Newspapers have insurance to meet claims but individuals do not, and so one good way of squashing a story is to sue the writer. The longer a case takes, the higher the costs. If the law is complex cases will take a while to resolve. Journalists need to know all this. But, as solicitor Tamsin Allen explains in the following article, there is a new defence available in the 2013 Defamation Act for academics who publish in journals.

Journalists in the UK must now swot up on the new Defamation Act, which came into force on the 1 January 2014. They also have to consider the old law in order to discern how the new legislation may make a difference in practice. Many of the commentaries on the new legislation agree that the old law will still be taken into account when courts consider new claims, at least for a while. It's not easy. The old law was made up of two Defamation Acts (1952 and 1996), plus an enormous amount of case law.

One of the main concerns was that defamation law, as it stood, favoured the protection of reputation over freedom of expression. Claimants had to do very little to succeed. They needed to show that material was published to a third party and that it was defamatory. They did not need to show any loss or harm. The burden fell on defendants to show why they should not be liable. This could be done using one of several

defences – including justification, fair comment and privilege.

So what will be the consequences of the new act? How much difference will it make to journalists? Claimants will now have to do more than before. Section 1 of the act states that a claimant must now show that the material either has caused, or is likely to cause, serious harm to his or her or its reputation. Where the claimant is an organisation that trades for profit, it will have to show serious financial harm. This section was designed to prevent frivolous claims. But courts had already devised a method of dealing with such claims. In the McLibel trial, McDonald's would have found it difficult to negotiate Section 1 when suing Helen Steel and Dave Morris for defamation. Steel and Morris were activists who handed out leaflets highly critical of the McDonald's operations outside a McDonald's burger restaurant. McDonald's sued for defamation even though it is hard to know how much harm the leaflets would cause to its business. McDonald's was successful insofar as the defendants could not prove the truth of the statements on the leaflets (although the pair later took the case to the European Court of Human Rights, which deemed they had been denied a fair trial under article 10). But under the 2013 act, McDonald's would have had to show that the material caused serious financial harm before being allowed to pursue the claim. Although Section 1 and other aspects of the act have been criticised as "cosmetic" by lawyer and academic Claire de Than, there may be a benefit in having this test set out in legislation as it is more accessible as law and may deter claimants more than a decision of the court.

However, many claims will easily surmount this hurdle. There have been several cases in which claims that would have met the test have been successful, only for the material complained of to be exposed later as entirely true – the case of the cyclist Lance Armstrong, for example. Armstrong

ABOVE: Science writer Simon Singh, left, with supporter David Davis MP, outside the High Court in London, after Singh won his Court of Appeal battle for the right to rely on the defence of fair comment in a libel action

vehemently denied taking any form of performance-enhancing drugs and successfully sued The Times. However, some years later Armstrong admitted the claims were true. Where claimants lie or persuade others to lie on their behalf, no amount of legislation or

## Defamation law, as it stood, favoured the protection of reputation over freedom of expression

improved defences will help – possibly not even the public interest defence. My journalism students are well aware that they must keep notebooks and other evidence, but sometimes they need to be convinced that other factors come into play when deciding whether to publish a story or defend a claim. The Lord McAlpine case was very useful on this point. In 2012 the BBC Newsnight programme broadcast an item that claimed to know the identity of a well-known figure involved in the abuse of residents of a children's home in north Wales. Although the programme did not actually name anyone, users on social-networking sites inferred that McAlpine – former deputy chairman of the Conservative party – was the accused. This was quickly shown to be entirely untrue, →

→ and McAlpine was successful in legal claims against the BBC, the comedian Alan Davies and Sally Bercow.

Trying to crystal-gaze how the courts will interpret the new statutory defences in the 2013 act is hard. In the past it was argued by many that the law never protected reputation or free speech. When the new legislation was finally given royal assent, Lord McNally claimed it would strike the correct balance between the two. It was hailed in the statement as an improvement, bringing an antiquated law into the 21$^{st}$ century.

Not everyone agrees. De Than says the act is merely codifying what courts have done already and achieves little else. Alastair Mullis and Andrew Scott in a recent article in the Modern Law Review also argue that the act has not addressed the right to reply or

## McDonald's would have to show that material caused serious financial harm before being allowed to pursue a claim

indeed the issue of what actually amounts to defamation. They say that because the courts will still have to use the old law to interpret the new, cases will not necessarily be shorter. Costs will not go down and there will not be a better balance between free speech and protection of reputation.

In trying to address the balance between freedom of speech and reputation, the legislation has gone some way towards redressing imbalance but fails to tackle effectively the issues of costs and remedies. ☒

© Lesley Phippen
www.indexoncensorship.org

**Lesley Phippen** is director of graduate studies at the Centre for Journalism, University of Kent, UK

## A hard act to follow

·····························································

*Britain's libel laws have had a makeover following an intense media campaign, but the changes might not be as profound as supporters hoped, argues lawyer* **Tamsin Allen**

Any law that adjudicates between the media and citizens is bound to be controversial. The Defamation Act 2013 came into force at the start of this year. It was the product of a remarkably intense political and media campaign. The Libel Reform Campaign hailed the act as "a fairer libel law, which would allow us to criticise and hold to account the rich and the powerful". According to the government, its aim is "to ensure that a fair balance is struck between the right to freedom of expression and the protection of reputation".

The most controversial elements of libel law are in the territory of newer relationships – between science bloggers and drug companies; individuals subjected to hate campaigns on social media or comment threads; large companies using reputation management professionals to silence their NGO critics. Will the act succeed in rebalancing the law to ensure fairness to both publishers and those on the receiving end of criticism? We need to wait for cases to be heard to see how the changes work in practice, but there is plenty to consider even now.

The act introduces a "serious harm" threshold. This is a statutory version of an existing common law convention that a libel should be sufficiently serious to warrant the issue of proceedings. Having it in black and white may help to discourage trivial claims, but this is not a substantive change. However, there is a change in the serious harm threshold for companies. The act states that "harm to the reputation of a body that trades for profit is not 'serious harm' unless it has caused or is likely to cause the body serious financial loss". What is serious – whether it includes damage to goodwill – has yet to be decided, but this is a significant and welcome development (except perhaps for very small companies, which will have an additional expensive hurdle to leap before being able to sue over damaging false allegations).

There are some other significant changes in the act. Section 8 introduces a single publication rule. It replaces the rule that every publication of defamatory material gives rise to a fresh cause of action that is subject to its own one-year limitation period. The old rule allowed claimants to sue archived website publications many years after first publication online, as every download constituted a "new" publication. Now claimants will be barred from suing more than a year after first publication (unless publication is in a substantially different medium). The court still has discretion not to apply the one-year limitation if it is just to do so – for example, where a claimant did not know that a version of a defamatory article had been archived and was still accessible – but the onus will be on the claimant to persuade the court.

The new defences in the act will require many years of judicial interpretation before they can be used as a simple tool by writers and publishers without lawyers. The new defence of "honest opinion" replaces the old "fair comment" defence, and is very similar; the defence of "truth" replaces the virtually identical common-law defence of justification. The "public interest" defence is based on an existing defence of "responsible journalism" but is different in some important ways. A publisher will be able to defend a statement that is on a matter of public interest and the publisher reasonably believed to be in the public interest. The concept of public interest itself is fluid. The act says that the court will look at all the circumstances of the case in deciding whether or not the defendant's belief that the statement was in the public interest was reasonable. It seems certain that the courts will look to the existing body of learning and the common law to help in interpretation, despite the abolition of the old defences. But how is the author of a community blog supposed to find out whether their remarks about the church hall funds are in the public interest? Should the author examine the accounts rather than relying on back copies of the parish magazine?

Section 12 is an attempt to provide an effective remedy for those who have been defamed, by giving the court the power to order publication of a summary of its judgment. This may be valuable for claimants and could help to reduce damages by helping to vindicate the claimant's reputation. Such summaries are likely to become standard in the majority of successful defamation actions.

In Section 6 there is also a new defence to protect scientists and academics publishing in peer-reviewed journals. The publication of a statement in such a journal is privileged, as long as certain conditions are met. This devel-

## Although claims brought by foreign claimants have hit the headlines, they are very small in number

opment is helpful and relatively uncontroversial – although most such publications would have been privileged under the old common law qualified privilege defences.

Section 9 of the act is intended to address the issue of libel tourism by introducing a new test for acceptance of jurisdiction in defamation cases by courts in England and Wales. It applies when a defamation action is brought against a person who is not domiciled in the UK, an EU member state or a state which is a party to the Lugano Convention. In such circumstances, the court must be satisfied that the UK is "clearly the most appropriate place in which to bring an action in respect of the statement". This section demonstrates parliament's intention to deal with the UK's reputation as libel capital of the world, and may have an impact on judges deciding on such claims. However, the civil →

→ courts had already developed guidance on choosing the most appropriate jurisdiction in numerous areas of law, so there were already rules to govern decision-making. Claims brought by people living in jurisdictions with corrupt or poorly functioning legal systems, or systems which do not comply with the European Convention on Human Rights, can still be heard in the UK, even if the claimant's connections with the UK are peripheral (providing the claimant has a reputation to be protected here and there was publication here). Although some claims brought by foreign claimants have hit the headlines, they are very small in number. The changes in this section are more to do with perception than reality.

Section 5 of the act creates a new defence for operators of websites who can show that they did not post the statement complained of (so it applies to comments posted by readers).

and there will be new case law defining the provisions in the 2013 act. Does it rebalance freedom of expression with the protection of reputation? It makes life easier for those writing in the public interest and for scientists, and more difficult for companies to use the libel laws to protect their reputations. But the new defences show how effectively our courts had already developed this balance. Of course, that development took many years and much expense before cases got to the Court of Appeal or Supreme Court. But the risk of codifying such defences is that future development becomes more difficult, not less. X

© Tamsin Allen
www.indexoncensorship.org

# The laws on website operators, hosts and search engines remains an impenetrable mess

But it is subject to a number of conditions and gives protection only to website operators who respond to a "notice of complaint", which must include details of the person posting the statement in question. The problem with this section is that it does not provide claimants with an effective route to deal with defamatory allegations made online, nor does it provide complete protection for website operators. It is inconsistent in some important ways with the E-Commerce Directive adopted in 2000 and it relies on regulations that can be changed, thus undermining the stated intention for clarity and foreseeability. The law on website operators, hosts and search engines remains an impenetrable mess.

As well as the previous defamation acts, a mass of existing case law will remain relevant,

**Tamsin Allen** is head of the media and law team at Bindmans LLP. She acts in a wide range of libel and privacy cases and has co-ordinated the group of claimants bringing legal action against News Group Newspapers for phone hacking

# Walls divide

43(3): 101/103 | DOI: 10.1177/0306422014548830

Chinese author Xiaolu Guo has long experience of censorship – and not just in her native land. She talks to **Jemimah Steinfeld**

**W**HEN XIAOLU GUO wrote about abortion in A Concise Chinese-English Dictionary for Lovers, her US publishing house wanted to remove the section for fear it would offend middle-class America. Guo was angry. Having written plenty of material that was censored in her home country of China, and with a brother who had participated in the 1989 Tiananmen Square protests, she knew well the limits to free expression back home. She was less aware of how censorship worked elsewhere.

Guo was born in 1973 and raised in a fishing village in south China. At 18 she moved to Beijing to study at the Beijing Film Academy and later began writing screenplays, fiction and criticism. Her first documentary, The Concrete Revolution, followed construction workers in the run-up to the 2008 Beijing Olympics. She now lives in Hackney, London.

"In China writers face political censorship. In the West artists are superficially more free, but then there is commercial censorship," says Guo. The dynamic between overt censorship and its more subtle manifestations forms the backbone of her latest novel, I Am China.

I Am China follows a punk musician in Beijing, Kublai Jian, and his poet lover Mu, who are separated by political disruptions, including China's Jasmine Revolution of 2011. Their story is pieced together by Iona Fitzpatrick, a Scottish woman in London, who translates a series of their letters and diaries for publication. Through Iona the narrative develops into a fragmented account of their lives and of the relationship between art and politics. We learn that Jian, who participated in the Tiananmen Square protests as a teenager, has since channelled his criticism of the Chinese government through music. It was at one of his concerts that he met Mu and fell in love. It was also at one of his concerts that he was arrested and later exiled – to become as much of an outcast in Europe as he was in China.

Guo sees elements of herself in all of the characters. Mu's father suffers from cancer, as Guo's own father did. Iona lives close to where Guo is now based in London and, like Guo, writes and communicates across languages and cultures. But it is Jian with whom she identifies first and foremost. "The energy of Jian – his anger, his character, he doesn't surrender – that is very much like my character," she says. Both she and Jian are "anarchists".

Jian's struggle for freedom of movement and expression is the most explicit engagement with censorship in the book. But it is not the only censorship mentioned. In one of the most powerful sections, Mu is attacked by a crowd of Chinese students at Harvard University when she recites Allen Ginsberg's 1956 poem America, originally published in his collection Howl, substituting "China" →

ABOVE: Chinese novelist and director Xiaolu Guo on the set of her 2011 film UFO In Her Eyes

→ for "America". Just a few verses in she's pulled off the stage and slapped in the face.

"They grabbed my arms exactly like the Red Guards had done to protesters during

## In China writers face political censorship. In the West there is commercial censorship

the Cultural Revolution. The only difference was that these little Red Guards were educated at Harvard, not in the rice fields of home," writes Mu, comparing Jian's earlier

silencing in China to the silencing of her on this stage thousands of miles away.

The lines quickly blur further. Western commercial censorship and Chinese political censorship become one. Iona's London publisher halts production of the book after Chinese pressure not to print. And even Iona struggles with the limitations of language. "How much liberty does a translator have?" she asks, while grappling with the letters.

Uniting different countries under the banner of censorship was important, says Guo: "I didn't just want to write only about China because China is part of the global evolution."

At the same time, in outlining what writers cannot talk about, Guo also highlights what they can do. Jian's overt activism is juxtaposed by Mu's softer approach. Through being less confrontational, the young poet can – and does – express more. As the pair clash over the role of art (for Jian "all art is political expression"; for Mu it's much more personal), the novel challenges Western assumptions about Chinese free speech.

Ironically it is Mu's character who is almost censored out. Iona is told by her publisher that Mu represents no more than a "lens" through which to present Jian's tale, because he is the one who fits the Western romantic notion of persecuted dissident, which is more likely to sell books.

This highlights Guo's other point. She says that "the state artist market needs to be more discussed" instead of overlooked as we focus almost exclusively on the bigger names, such as Ai Weiwei. Guo has written in defence of Chinese state writers, a label given to those who are considered to work without challenging the rules of the government. Then there are non-state artists who won't work within the rules and will therefore take bigger risks (and have become more notorious in the West). However, as Guo points out, the lines blur – because both non-state artists might have started off following the rules, and state artists might very subtly challenge the system. She specifically mentions Mo Yan, whose winning of the Nobel Prize for Literature in 2012 invited a lot of criticism about why someone working within the confines of the Chinese state could be valued. But Guo points out that the lines between those considered "state artists" and those who aren't are often blurred, as both may challenge the system in different ways.

"But surely every artist is born from within a state, trained by the state, and has a complex discourse with the state, even an artistic reliance on it, until the day the state choses to designate that artist an ideological enemy," she writes on her blog.

In some ways this reappraisal of the mechanisms of censorship is liberating, and Guo's own art has evolved into a pastiche of the styles of Jian and Mu. As she adds on the topic: "Don't always look at China in terms of GDP and political talk. If you look at the literature, music and art scene in China you will see that it is rich, interesting, incredible. Once you enter there you have a softer landing towards Chinese culture." 🅇

© Jemimah Steinfeld
www.indexoncensorship.org

**Jemimah Steinfeld** is a contributing editor to Index on Censorship and is the author of upcoming book Little Emperors and Material Girls: Sex and Youth in Modern China. She tweets @JFSteinfeld

# Taking a pop

43(3): 104/106 | DOI: 10.1177/0306422014548358

South Korean artist Lee Ha talks to **Steven Borowiec** about his recent arrests and why the authorities in Seoul are not amused by his art

**B**Y PUBLICLY POKING fun at some of South Korea's most recognisable political figures, Lee Ha has built a reputation as his country's most troublemaking political pop artist. Clashes with the authorities over his art have become a way of life for the 46-year-old.

Lee is a pioneer of political satire in South Korea. While political art was an important part of the country's democratisation movement in the late 1980s, the images then tended to be no-nonsense calls for freedom and civil rights. In his work, Lee has taken an irreverent approach, using cartoonish styles and wild colours.

His latest antics come at a time of particular public sensitivity as South Korea is still reeling from its worst-ever peacetime disaster. In April, the Sewol ferry sunk, killing more than 300 people, most of them school children. The government was criticised for failing to regulate the shipping industry properly, for allowing an unsafe vessel to leave port dangerously overloaded and for reacting too late when disaster struck.

Lee responded to the national grieving with an image of President Park Geun-hye, clad in traditional Korean attire, smiling as the Sewol sank behind her, surrounded by seven dogs, one representing each member of her cabinet. In Korea, describing a person or thing as "doglike" is a harsh insult.

In his other infamous image, he depicted President Park as a kind of geriatric Snow White with a bulbous, oversized head, holding an apple, which has a portrait of her father, the late President Park Chung-hee, set in a heart-shaped window.

South Korea is generally ruled by Confucian norms, where it's taboo for someone to openly criticise someone older than themselves, and it is especially rare for personal attacks to be made in public. Many, therefore, find Lee's images offensive. But beyond gasping in shock, there is not much the authorities can do to stop him, besides regularly dragging him into court and hoping he gets fed up and quits of his own accord.

Lee says he's never been convicted of anything, but he has been charged 30 times, indicted three times and brought in for questioning by police countless times. His first indictment came in 2012 when he was charged with illegal advertising after he posted an unflattering image of the former South Korean president Chun Doo-hwan, a military strongman who ruled from 1980-88, holding a cheque for a little less than $300. At the time, Chun was a subject of controversy for claiming that he was unable to repay the millions he stole from state coffers as president, saying he had only a few hundred dollars to his name.

Part of what has got Lee into trouble is his insistence on displaying his work outdoors. Instead of keeping his images inside galleries in well-to-do neighbourhoods, Lee prefers to

ABOVE: Lee Ha's caricatures of the 2012 presidential candidates resulted in arrest, but not conviction

put them up in public, on walls and at bus stops in busy urban areas. By making his work visible to more people, he hopes to spur a conversation on aspects of Korean society he thinks should be addressed.

"Nowadays we have a lot of serious social problems, like corruption and inequality. We need to reflect on the unpleasant reality," Lee says.

Lee was acquitted after his legal representatives argued that the poster could not be considered advertising because there were no products or services mentioned in the image.

In late 2012 Lee was charged with violating the special election law after putting up posters that showed caricatures of the opposition candidates running against Park for the presidency. The law prohibits the dissemination of materials in support or detraction of a candidate 180 days before the vote, but

## He depicted President Park as a kind of geriatric Snow White with a bulbous, oversized head

Lee was not convicted because the Supreme Court considered his works contained no clear political message.  →

ABOVE: Lee Ha's portrait of South Korea's president, Park Geun-hye, with the Sewol ferry sinking behind her and seven dogs representing her cabinet members

→   The third indictment was for the image of President Park as Snow White, for which Lee was acquitted in June.

Lee's arrests have taken place against a backdrop of declining freedom of expression in South Korea. In 2011, South Korea's Freedom House press freedom ranking fell from "free" to "partly free" and has remained there ever since. In knocking South Korea down a notch, the Washington-based watchdog pointed to "increasing official censorship, particularly of online content, as well as the government's attempt to influence media outlets' news and information content".

Similar criticisms were made by the United Nations' special rapporteur for human rights defenders, Margaret Sekaggya, when she visited Seoul in June 2013.

The country is admired overseas for its lightning-fast internet connections, but South Koreans do not enjoy unfettered access to the web. Freedom House put South Korea 20th out of the 60 countries in its report on internet freedom. It was described as "partly free", the same category as Nigeria, Brazil and Angola.

Though Lee is still not much known outside Korea, an exhibition in the US has raised his international profile. In the spring of 2011 Lee's depictions of world leaders were exhibited in New York under the title Pretty Dictators versus Pretty Leaders. The exhibition included an image of US President Barack Obama as a smiling Rambo figure with an assault rifle and a portrait of Osama Bin Laden cradling a fluorescent green lamb.

His experiences in and out of court over the past few years have Lee convinced that the nation's authorities are simply harassing him with the hope that he will eventually shut up.

Lee thinks he is being made an example of for other artists, a sign of the struggles that follow any overt criticism of those in power.

"My case isn't just about me – it's important for all artists and creative people in Korea," Lee said. "By trying to intimidate me, the government is trying to keep everyone quiet and scared. They're trying to send the message that one can't be outwardly critical and keep one's freedoms." ☒

© Steven Borowiec
www.indexoncensorship.org

**Steven Borowiec** is a journalist based in South Korea. He tweets @steven_borowiec

# Mapping media threats

43(3): 107/109 | DOI: 10.1177/0306422014549928

Attacks on journalists in the Balkans are being highlighted by Index on Censorship's European map of media freedom. **Melody Patry** and **Milana Knezevic** report on the findings and consider the rising suppression of freedom of speech in the region

**N**ENAD TOMIC, EDITOR-IN-CHIEF of Serbian news site Ruma, was visiting a hotel when a businessman threatened to cut off his nose and ears. Tomic, who had been reporting on the man's business affairs, is far from the only journalist with a first-hand account of the Balkans' problematic relationship with media freedom.

Index on Censorship and Osservatorio Balcani e Caucaso (OBC) launched an online platform in May to report and map media freedom violations in the European Union and across candidate countries until January 2015. Eight regional correspondents have been dedicated to monitoring what is happening across Europe, and the public has also been encouraged to submit reports. So far, over 250 cases have been reported. Almost half of the violations have been reported from the Balkans.

Of course, it is unwise to jump to conclusions based on crowdsourced data. Nonetheless, the numerous reports of censorship, verbal harassment and physical violence paint a worrying picture (see map on the next page). And, as reported on p91 of this magazine, the Organisation for Security and Cooperation in Europe (OSCE) representative on freedom of the media, Dunja Mijatović, is also worried about threats in the region.

The latest Reporters Without Borders Press Freedom Index reports that Serbia ranks 54 out of 180 (where one – Finland – is the gold standard). Bosnia and Croatia are not far behind, at 65 and 66 respectively. Kosovo is 80th and Albania 85th, with Montenegro and Macedonia trailing at 114th and 123rd. Slovenia, in 34th position, is in line with many of the current EU countries and its score raises the region's average. But the rankings are concerning for Croatia, which is already an EU member and for the other countries – including Serbia, Bosnia and the smaller Balkan states – that aspire to join.

Concerns about the state of media freedom have to be seen within the context of the region's poor economy. There is also corruption and lack of accountability within the political systems, and significant power is granted to wealthy tycoons. Serbian journalist Ana Jovovic* told Index: "Because the economy in Serbia is very bad, it is easy to control the media. There is no resistance either from journalists or editors. They are only looking for a way to survive."

In Macedonia, the country's latest European Commission progress report also expresses concern about the lack of transparency over the allocation of government advertising, highlighting claims that they →

# A SELECTION OF PRESS CENSORSHIP INCIDENTS IN THE BALKANS, TAKEN FROM INDEX ON CENSORSHIP AND OSSERVATORIO BALCANI E CAUCASO'S CROWDSOURCING PROJECT.

YOU CAN EXPLORE THE FULL DATABASE – AND REPORT CASES – AT MEDIAFREEDOM.USHAHIDI.COM

## MONTENEGRO

A journalist and photographer from Dnevne novine newspaper took photos of a suspected criminal in Podgorica, and was then intimidated by a small group and forced to delete the images.

DATE OF INCIDENT: JUNE 2014

## BOSNIA AND HERZEGOVINA

Slavo Kukic, a prominent writer and columnist, was severely beaten with a baseball bat in his office.

DATE OF INCIDENT: JUNE 2014

## SERBIA

Serbian government accused of censoring blogs and articles that were critical of the state's handling of devastating floods. An article on news site Blic, suggesting that the prime minister should resign, removed without explanation.

DATE OF INCIDENT: MAY 2014

## CROATIA

Journalist Drago Pilsel received threatening message on Facebook after publishing an article about a convicted war criminal's release from prison.

DATE OF INCIDENT: JUNE 2014

## MACEDONIA

Journalists working for Macedonian Nova TV, Radio Free Europe and Fokus magazine were reporting from a protest in Skopje, when the local police forced them to delete photos and videos.

DATE OF INCIDENT: MAY 2014

Map design by Brett Evans Biedscheid (statetostate.co.uk)

→ are "directed only towards pro-government media". There are also worries about the influence of big business on journalism. For instance, Bosnia's biggest construction magnate Fahrudin Radoncic, also owns the country's most widely read daily newspaper, Dnevni Avaz, and has served as a minister of security between 2012 and 2014. The number of powerful business owners who have side interests in media companies constitutes a major obstacle to media pluralism and independence.

Though there are ongoing threats and violence against critical journalists in the region, most incidents have not been properly investigated and the response from the authorities has been minimal. This environment of impunity has contributed to creating a climate of fear and self-censorship. Zeljko Ivanovic, co-founder and co-owner of Vijesti news site, where journalists have been physically attacked, wrote in a blog for Index last October: "Not only have none of these criminal acts been properly investigated, but the authorities and their institutions have done everything in their power to render the investigations meaningless and to ensure that real culprits are not touched."

Ilcho Cvetanoski, Index's regional correspondent in the Balkans for the crowd-sourcing project, added: "Keeping in mind the number of unresolved assaults from previous years, being a professional journalist in this region is not an easy job. This atmosphere of impunity is probably the biggest threat to media freedom."

Press freedom in the region has long been complicated. Under communism, despite the relatively liberal and free Yugoslav model, there were still restrictions on what journalists could report. Propaganda and hate speech disseminated through the media also played some part in the violence that enveloped parts of the region in the 1990s. Award-winning Bosnian journalist Kemal Kurspahic wrote an acclaimed book called Prime Time Crime: Balkan Media in War and Peace in which he accuses certain media in Serbia, Croatia and later Bosnia of "perpetrating lies about genocidal threats, awakening forgotten fears and hatreds, and preparing once peaceful neighbours to suspect, hate, confront, and finally, kill each other in the last decade of the 20th century".

# Being a journalist in this region is not an easy job. The atmosphere of impunity is the biggest threat to media freedom

Jovovic believes that in order for the situation to improve, the government must withdraw from the media. But, she says, international players also have a role, especially at EU level: "In my opinion, European politicians should insist more often on media freedoms and on the government's withdrawal from media ownership."

Index's online platform, with the crowd-sourced map, is a project mainly funded by the European Commission. It will serve not only to monitor incidents but also as an advocacy tool to help raise awareness of media freedom in the region and give European officials more leverage to tackle the issue. ⊠

*Name changed to protect the individual*

© Milana Knezevic and Melody Patry
www.indexoncensorship.org

**Milana Knezevic** is editorial assistant at Index on Censorship
**Melody Patry** is senior advocacy officer at Index on Censorship

# Holed up in Harare

43(3): 110/114 | DOI: 10.1177/0306422014548623

Reporting from Zimbabwe is a dangerous business. **Natasha Joseph** talks to those that walk the line

**I**N DARK SUIT trousers, a blue collared shirt and maroon tie, bespectacled and wearing a plaid jacket, Edmund Kudzayi, 28, didn't look much like a terrorist during a mid-June appearance at the High Court in Zimbabwe's capital, Harare.

But, if the state is to be believed, that's precisely what the young editor of the Sunday Mail is: at the time of going to press, he's been charged with "attempting to commit an act of insurgency, banditry, sabotage or terrorism". The Zanu-PF government claims he favours verbal bombs and is the mastermind behind the mysterious Facebook page Baba Jukwa, which offers startling insights into the machinations of Zanu-PF.

To understand how a blogger can get so far up politicians' noses, you must understand just how limited access to information is under Zimbabwe's draconian press legislation. It is a criminal offence to insult President Robert Mugabe or the country's powerful security operatives. A constitutional court challenge to the insult law by civil society groups was successful. However, this ruling has been appealed and, while that process is under way, the government continues to use the insult laws. If Kudzayi is convicted of the offences with which he's been charged he faces life behind bars.

So when Baba Jukwa was born, so to speak, in early 2013, it sparked an information revolution. Within weeks of establishing his Facebook blog it had about 200,000

"likes". By July, the figure was nearly 500,000. (That's far more than Mugabe has, incidentally.) Soon after Baba Jukwa's emergence, the South African daily newspaper Business Day reported: "Baba Jukwa's name is whispered in buses, bars and on street corners by Zimbabweans eager for the inside scoop on President Robert Mugabe's ruling party. One avid follower even climbs a tree in a rural village, awaiting a signal to call a friend for the latest tidbits from the mysterious yet stupendously popular blogger." Baba Jukwa – the name means "Jukwa's father" in the Shona language which is widely spoken across Zimbabwe – appeared in the months leading up to the country's 2013 national elections and, claiming to be a disgruntled Zanu-PF member, told tales of corruption and ineptitude within the governing party. He signs off each post with "*Asijiki*", another Shona term which means "We do not retreat".

And certainly, Baba Jukwa – if indeed he is a single person, for the posts are written in vastly varying styles despite that standard sign-off – doesn't seem the retreating sort. When state-run media reported that Mugabe had traveled to Singapore for an eye check-up, Baba Jukwa responded by stating baldly that the 90-year-old statesman had once again travelled to the East for chemotherapy. It is widely believed within Zimbabwe and outside its borders that Mugabe is suffering from prostate cancer. →

ABOVE: A prison warden checks the documents of Sunday Mail editor Edmund Kudzayi, before releasing him from the Harare Magistrates Court after he was granted bail on July 4, 2014

→ The Sunday Mail's offices were raided on a Thursday morning in June and Kudzayi was taken into custody. Zanu-PF ministers insist he is Baba Jukwa, though they are equally adamant that he hasn't been working alone. Baba Jukwa fell silent in the days following Kudzayi's arrest. On 22 June he wrote: "Good morning Zimbabwe. Please say a short simple prayer to God in your own mother tongue, so our nation can be blessed, and there can be more exposures of evils and all hidden treacheries, we are now almost there now, just one small step left! *Asijiki*! *Ndatenda* [thank you] – Baba Jukwa."

On 3 July, the same day that Kudzayi was released on bail, Baba Jukwa wrote: "Cde Edmund has done nothing wrong please acquit him and let him serve the nation *Asijiki*! *Ndatenda*. Baba Jukwa."

## The history of state media is that it is weak and timid, sings praise for Zanu-PF, and only reports on the president's trips and government policies

Suggest to Zimbabwean journalists, though, that Kudzayi is the victim of a witch-hunt, and you begin to understand that there are far more complex dynamics at play. A senior Zimbabwean journalist based in South Africa – who, like all the reporters interviewed for this piece asked to remain anonymous for safety reasons – explains: "It's actually Zanu-PF's factional battle playing out through the media. Zanu has three factions, all jostling to succeed Mugabe," she says. The governing party's electoral congress is set for December 2014, and Mugabe, who has ruled Zimbabwe since it gained independence from Britain in 1980, seems finally poised to retire. His rhetoric remains as fiery as ever, but his ailing health has

opened the door for factions within the party to put their own candidates forward – and to use the country's newspapers to further their own ambitions. The senior journalist continues: "One faction is led by Vice President Joyce Mujuru, another by Justice Minister Emmerson Mnangagwa and the third by the military generals. All deny the existence of these factions, but these are well-known facts.

"Information Minister Jonathan Moyo belongs to the military camp. He's not keen on Mujuru succeeding Mugabe. Since his reappointment as information minister, he is accused by the Mujuru faction of attempting to weaken it by fighting through the media."

Moyo – who did not respond to requests for comment on this piece – is an intriguing figure. He's the architect of some of Zimbabwe's most restrictive press laws and so publicly reviled by Mugabe that the president in early 2014 referred to him as "a weevil, a fool and a devil incarnate". Moyo served as Zanu-PF's information minister first from 2000 to 2005, during a wave of crackdowns on media freedom, and was then expelled from the party after refusing to reserve a seat in his native Tsholotsho district for a woman candidate as decreed by Zanu-PF. Instead he ran for the seat himself as an independent candidate and won it. He served as an independent until 2009, when he returned to Zanu-PF, and took up his old cabinet position again last year.

The senior journalist goes on: "Moyo made surprise appointments to the Sunday Mail and Chronicle newspapers that fall under the Zimpapers stable. Zimpapers is state-owned and all the papers in its stable are state-controlled. The two surprises relate to Edmund Kudzayi and Mduduzi Mathuthu as editors of Sunday Mail and Chronicle. It was a surprise because Kudzayi once ran an anti-Zanu-PF news website out of the UK, where he lived, and Mathuthu ran an equally anti-government news website, www.NewZimbabwe.com.

Moyo also made appointments at a more junior level of people who have been considered to be anti-establishment.

With these appointments, the tone of state-owned newspapers "changed", the journalist explains. "They broke a series of huge stories on corruption now commonly known as 'salarygate' in Zimbabwe. They exposed how CEOs at government parastatals were earning obscene salaries, presiding over non-functional decaying entities."

It was a case of a docile, large dog that's always wagged its tail no matter how hard its master beats it suddenly sinking its teeth into a raised hand.

"The history of state media is that it is weak and timid, sings praise for Zanu-PF, and only reports on the president's trips and government policies only," the journalist says. But there was a worm at the heart of the apple.

"The stories only exposed allies of Mujuru or those ministers who are aligned to her and who oversee these parastatals. Mujuru then complained in various briefings to Mugabe and her team put together dossiers they gave to the president. She complained that the reports in the same government media were only serving to destroy Zanu-PF from within – anger about the decaying economy was being directed at the party by ordinary people," the journalist said.

The Zimbabwean bureau of the South Africa-based Mail & Guardian reported that the media was discussed at a Zanu-PF politburo meeting on 4 June. The politburo is the party's highest decision-making body: the paper reported that Moyo was "attacked" by his colleagues for appointing Kudayi and Mathuthu and effectively ordered to sack them. He was also "openly accused" of using the media to stage factional fights.

It was Moyo's refusal to fire Kudzayi that saw Mugabe use his platform at a funeral to verbally attack his own information minister. Moyo subsequently apologised during a meeting with the president and kept his

job. Days later, Kudzayi and Mathuthu's homes were broken into and the former was arrested.

I understand that Kudzayi has been under watch by intelligence on the instigation of the Mujuru faction.

The Committee for the Protection of Journalists (CPJ) is hugely worried about the situation in Zimbabwe. The committee's Africa programme coordinator, Sue Valentine, says that Kudzayi's arrest and the "extremely harsh charges" he faces are likely to have a "chilling effect on all journalists" – and, of course, deny Zimbabweans of their right to information. Asked to put Index on Censorship in touch with some reporters who

# Journalists who do not wish to end up behind bars or find themselves under scrutiny by Zimbabwe's security forces must put their heads down

might be willing to speak on strict condition of anonymity, the senior journalist replied that this would be difficult – "there is always unwillingness because the environment is altogether rather poisoned".

The reality, of course, is that whatever factional battles are being played out in news pages and on newspaper's websites, journalists who do not wish to end up behind bars or find themselves under scrutiny by Zimbabwe's notorious security forces must simply put their heads down and continue to work. A 30-year-old reporter who contributes to several publications inside and outside Zimbabwe under pseudonyms, explains that the desire for anonymity is two-fold. He worked as a teacher for some years because a dearth of publications, particularly those not owned by the state, meant there were very few jobs for reporters. After six years in →

→ the industry, he says, the money hasn't improved at all. His pseudonym also gives him the space he needs to "write exposes about government operations – by not using your real name, you stay safe".

How safe is debatable. He is almost flippant about being threatened in the line of duty, both in person and via emails. He's also been followed, he says – a bid, he believes, to send the message that "we're watching you".

## It has become a minefield for journalists and editors to do their work impartially without being viewed as being in the "camp" of a politician

Kudzayi's arrest concerns him on one level: "The editor is meant to be the last line of defence for a publication but if the editor is harassed it means the journalist on the ground is worse off because normally editors have security personnel at their homes." But, he continues, "I'm not frightened." He reads Kudzayi's arrest precisely as his colleague and the CPJ's Valentine do: factionalism springing from Zanu-PF's politburo meetings on to the pages of newspapers and then into life on the streets of Zimbabwe.

Teldah Mawarire, the Mail & Guardian's Zimbabwean editor, says there's plenty to worry about. "The environment becomes more difficult for journalists to navigate because in addition to the existing repressive laws, journalists now also have to navigate around factions and find ways to steer clear of these political agendas being pushed from the top. It has become a minefield for journalists and editors to do their work impartially without being viewed as being in the 'camp' of one politician or the other. It's also very unhealthy to have that (unstated but very obvious) policy that journalists who have been employed in the private media

must never be appointed to public media positions. The harassment of the editors has also brought to light the issue that has been raised for a long time now – Zanu-PF as a political party must not be dictating to the public media what to do and who to cover. The public media is not a mouthpiece for the party so the party's politburo must not be discussing the firing of editors. That is inconsistent with democratic norms."

Despite the low salary, the harassment and the climate of fear in which Zimbabwean journalists operate, the young reporter remains remarkably upbeat. Baba Jukwa is just one example of the spirit of invention which he sees emerging in the country's guarded media landscape. "Everyone is a publisher now – Facebook and Twitter have become sources of information and there are more online newspapers, as well as new players in the newspaper industry like the Zimbabwe Mail and the reopened Daily News," he says.

"I love journalism. I would never leave the profession or trade it for anything."

*Asijiki*, indeed. X

© Natasha Joseph
www.indexoncensorship.org

**Natasha Joseph** is the news editor at the Johannesburg-based City Press newspaper. She tweets @tashjoeza

# Burma's "new" media face threats and attack

43(3): 115/117 | DOI: 10.1177/0306422014548666

With an election in Burma next year, **Wendy Law-Yone**, whose father ran an independent newspaper in the 1950s, looks at the challenges journalists still face in the aspiring democracy

**B**URMESE JOURNALISTS HAVE been harassed, intimidated, interrogated, arrested and handed down harsh prison sentences this year. Their treatment has cast grave doubt on the government's commitment to press reform, and spells hard times ahead for "new" media, especially as the country gears up for a potentially volatile general election next year.

In July, four reporters and the chief executive of the now-closed news weekly Unity Journal were sentenced to 10 years in prison with hard labour for reporting on the alleged manufacture of chemical weapons in a military facility in central Burma. The two dozen journalists who later staged a silent protest against the convictions, all dressed in Don't Kill Press T-shirts, with tape across their lips, have now been charged with unlawful assembly.

These shocking prison sentences, condemned by citizens' groups and press watchdogs alike, are the culmination of months of clamping down on the press. Since the beginning of this year, not only journalists but editors and publishers of privately owned newspapers, such as The Irrawaddy, have been called in for government questioning about their balance sheets. They have been made to justify even the names of their publications. A

reporter from the Democratic Voice of Burma was sentenced to a year in prison following an interview with an education official, who later brought charges of "trespassing" and "disturbing a civil servant while on duty".

Interference of this sort still seems mild in comparison to the repression of previous decades, when military authority took on the trappings of a police state. It was early in that era of totalitarian rule that my father, Ed Law-Yone, founder and publisher of The Nation, then the leading English-language daily newspaper, was imprisoned for five years – two in solitary confinement. In the absence of due process, there was no charge, no trial, no visiting rights for the prisoner's family, just indefinite incarceration for unspecified crimes.

For my father and his newspaper contemporaries, General Ne Win's military coup in 1962 marked the end of what seems in retrospect a golden age of press freedom, when despite chaos, corruption, treachery, larceny, inefficiency and a host of other evils besetting the government, the independent press was still allowed to flourish. In the period of parliamentary democracy between independence in 1948 and the coup, close to a hundred newspapers were published in Burmese and English, and in a variety of other →

ABOVE: A man reads a newspaper in front of a police van in Rangoon, Burma

→ languages: Chinese, Hindi, Gujarati, Urdu, Tamil and Telugu.

It did not mean that there were no attempts at censorship. In 1957, in the hey-

## In July, journalists were sentenced for 10 years with hard labour for reporting on the alleged manufacture of chemical weapons

day of his newspaper's influence, my father was charged with criminal libel for accusing

senior ministers in the U Nu government of corruption.

In a celebrated case, which he further dramatised by defending himself in court and then devoting large sections of his newspaper to the proceedings, my father established himself as a flamboyant champion of the free press. And although he lost his case, his jail sentence of one month was struck down on appeal, his fine reduced to a nominal sum, with a warning to "keep the peace and be of good behaviour" – allowing him to concede a Pyrrhic victory to his legal opponents.

Six years later though, when General Ne Win's henchmen came to arrest him, there was no law to invoke, no higher authority to appeal to, no cadre of newspapermen who could come to his aid because most of them were in jail. It was the beginning of decades of repression, of which extreme censorship was a significant feature.

Since President Thein Sein took office in 2011 exiled journalists have returned, hundreds of political prisoners have been released and new press laws drafted. In a society long deprived of steady access to reliable news, the sudden proliferation of independent daily newspapers in Burma, forbidden for some 50 years, has been greeted with jubilation and the "newspaper renaissance" welcomed as another step forward on the promised path to reform.

Yet there continue to be steady curbs on press freedom, curbs justified in the name of peace, security, religion and race, as anti-Muslim violence continues to erupt throughout the country.

Take the common Burmese fear and hatred of the Rohingya, the mostly Muslim people of Arakan in the west. The violence against them has led to the displacement of 100,000. The death toll has been uncertain; aid workers have been evicted from the area by local and central authorities and the besieged Rohingya incarcerated in concentration camps. Death threats have been issued to any witnesses suspected of pro-Muslim sympathies, including reporters.

Mob hysteria has been fuelled by fascist elements led by the Buddhist monk U Wirathu, founder of the extremist 969 movement. Violence has also been stoked by pro-government vigilantes. Meanwhile President Thein Sein blames the conflicts on the "misuse of new-found media freedoms". He has conflated inflammatory propaganda spread by social media with the reports of responsible journalists. Similar attempts to undermine the free press will no doubt continue in the run-up to the 2015 general election.

According to The Irrawaddy newspaper, Phoe Thaukkyar, vice-chairman of the interim Mynamar Press Council, has warned that the government is actively shrinking the space for independent media after a two-year period of relative freedom.

Opposition leader Aung San Suu Kyi has campaigned without success for a constitutional amendment that would allow her to run for president.

# President Thein Sein blames extremist conflicts on the "misuse of new-found media freedoms"

Under the existing constitution, she is ineligible to run because of a clause that prohibits anyone with a foreign spouse or child. Her party, the National League for Democracy, has announced that it will contest the 2015 elections regardless.

In their coverage of the intensely scrutinised contest, Burmese journalists will be facing formidable, hydra-headed forms of censorship. We can only hope that in the event, with the world's eyes on Burma, the government will be a little less ready to hit the kill switch. ⊠

© Wendy Law-Yone
www.indexoncensorship.org

**Wendy Law-Yone** is a Burmese-born journalist and novelist, whose recent memoir is published in the US as A Daughter's Memoir of Burma (Columbia University Press). She tweets @wendylawyone

# Should Hitler's Mein Kampf be republished?

**OPINION: HEAD TO HEAD**

43(3): 118/121 | DOI: 10.1177/0306422014549296

The German copyright on Mein Kampf expires in 2015, renewing debate on whether it should reprinted, or even read. **Sascha Feuchert**, an expert in Holocaust literature and vice president of German PEN, believes an academic version is vital. **Charlotte Knobloch**, former vice president of the World Jewish Congress, says it should be illegal

## Charlotte Knobloch

I am firmly of the conviction that Mein Kampf should never again be legal and it should not be made publically available, in any shape or form, in Germany or anywhere else in the world. [In Germany, it is currently legal to own existing copies.] It is one of the most offensive anti-semitic diatribes that has ever been written. It is a

ABOVE: Charlotte Knobloch

dangerous book that unleashed unspeakable devastation. This book formed the ideological basis that paved the way to the industrial operation that was the mass extermination of the European Jews: the Holocaust. It is a Pandora's box: when you stir up this kind of hatred, no one knows where it might lead.

## Sascha Feuchert

Obnoxious, repellent, abominable: there can be no doubt that Mein Kampf is one of the most hideous texts in the German language. Characterised by racial hatred and a relentless urge to crush all dissent, it is also driven by Hitler's desire to provide his acolytes with a manual on how to seize power and consolidate it through brute force.

It is a normal, healthy reflex to want to delete

ABOVE: Sascha Feuchert

this work once and for all from our cultural memory, so that it can never again spread its disturbing message. But when the copyright expires in Germany in 2015, 70 years after the dictator's death, it makes sense and, indeed, is of utmost importance that a critical academic edition is readily available in its original language as source material. The

Munich-based Institute for Contemporary History (Institut für Zeitgeschichte, IfZ) is currently working to produce such an edition, with the aim of publishing it in January 2016, although funding for the project has recently been withdrawn by the state of Bavaria, which holds the current copyright.

The discussion of whether German readers should be "allowed" access to the text is a farce. Even though it has been illegal to print and distribute the work in Germany since 1945, the book has been freely accessible online for years, both in German and in countless translations: a quick Google search brings up the required results. Follow the links, however, and you'll find an unannotated edition, devoid of context, or, most likely, end up on a far-right website. A scholarly edition could offer a serious alternative – especially for younger readers – which contextualises the content, deconstructs the stylised autobiography, reveals the many amendments made to the text up to the final edition in 1945, and documents Hitler's countless false assertions. It would, of course, be essential that this scholarly edition is also freely available on the internet and as easy to find as the many other versions of the work that do not offer all of this additional context. The academics in Munich have still not decided whether to publish an open-access version online or just a printed version. If they do not wish to undermine their own claim of wanting to educate readers, then this edition has to be published freely on the internet.

## Charlotte Knobloch

Of course, it is impossible to prevent people from finding the text on the internet, but there is a considerable difference between the text being found only on controversial websites, which are relevant only to their intended audience, and the book once again being freely and widely stocked in bookstores and libraries across Germany. There are people who are considering publishing the book, or parts of it, for academic reasons, but others have commercial motivations. "Hitler sells" is the age-old axiom that has prompted countless tasteless artefacts in the past.

## Sascha Feuchert

Reading Mein Kampf helps you to "make sense of Hitler's perspective on the world, his ideological roots, his contradictions and, ultimately, the consequences of his aims", as historian Andreas Wirsching, director of the Institute for Contemporary History, puts it. If you really want to understand the Third Reich, then you have to go back to the sources, and there is no room here for taboos. The Bavarian government, to whom the copyright for Hitler's writings was transferred by US occupation forces after

# If you really want to understand the Third Reich, then you have to go back to the sources, and there is no room here for taboos

the war, may have withdrawn from financing the project – mainly due to protest from Holocaust survivors in Israel – but they have not recalled the finances already allocated or made any other steps towards blocking the project. On the contrary, they have repeatedly assured the scholars at the Institute for Contemporary History that their academic freedom will not be affected.

There is, then, recognition on a political level of the benefits of making this source text available. And yet the state of Bavaria has also made a contrary statement to the effect that after expiry of the copyright, they would employ all legal means to prevent the dissemination of the book, if it were used to "incite racial hatred". State ministers of justice across Germany have since aligned →

→ themselves with this position. It looks like politicians trying to do the splits. On the one hand, there's the educational value that an academic edition can offer, and then there's the well-intentioned goal of wanting to "protect" the public from the dissemination of the text and its inhumane ideas. Time will tell whether German judges will follow the approach taken by the politicians, who want to emphasise the principle that there is no place in Germany for context-free, unscholarly editions; not every Tom, Dick and Harry should be able to publish their own version of Mein Kampf after the copyright expires. And meanwhile, absurdly enough, the Bavarian government has also said that even the IfZ edition would be vetted for its potential for incitement.

### Charlotte Knobloch

No one who's interested in German history is reliant on reading Mein Kampf. Far from

## To argue there's a case for reading the text to understand the historic context is a rather spurious assertion and certainly not very constructive

it. There are already a number of historical editions. Research on the topic has been outstanding and is very widely published. Every year more and more material is added to the corpus. And that's a good thing. We have certainly not completed the task of assessing the context and consequences of German history: there is still much to be done in terms of reappraising and exploring its many political, moral, economic, cultural, social and psychological dimensions. But Mein Kampf doesn't bring us a single step further. To argue there's a case for reading the text to understand the historic context is a rather spurious assertion and certainly not very constructive.

### Sascha Feuchert

There is an urgent need to demystify the book in Germany. There is no end to the legends and urban myths that spring up about the text, such as the much-repeated claim that while Mein Kampf had sold around 12 million copies by the end of the war, it was mostly an unread bestseller. A new edition could highlight longstanding evidence that the book enjoyed an extremely wide ownership from very early on and the readers should therefore have known full well about the planned extermination of the Jews and the designs Hitler had for dictatorship. Moreover, it is equally important that a new edition demonstrates something else that has recently been proven: the text itself does not have any intrinsic power to "infect" its readers. All of Hitler's speeches have been available for some years now, with extensive commentary, in an edition produced by IfZ. In content and in rhetoric they do not differ much from Mein Kampf, and yet these texts have certainly not unleashed any kind of "political epidemic". But Hitler's first book is to this day viewed with fear. This fear is irrational, as a stand-up comedian in Germany has demonstrated. The Turkish-born performer Serdar Somuncu has, since 1996, given more than 1,400 public readings of Mein Kampf across Germany, particularly in schools, which have been attended by some 250,000 people. The readings reveal the internal contradictions and follies of the book in a humorous, and yet very meaningful, way.

### Charlotte Knobloch

Hatred of people always has the power to infect others with hatred. As far as I'm concerned, the idea that the text needs demystifying only serves to add greater mystery and intrigue to it. I can see nothing of the kind in the text; it is a diatribe against Jews of the most revolting kind, which opened the floodgates for an ideology of mass destruction.

It is certainly not a violation of freedom of expression to prohibit the publication of Mein Kampf. On the contrary: the prevailing legal opinion on the matter says that publishing the original text is tantamount to the criminal act of incitement of racial hatred. There must be academic freedom to pursue research interests, and academic institutions will probably want to bring out an annotated version, even though I would personally prefer that they didn't. But at least this will not be subsidised by the state of Bavaria. The State Government have decided that much. ☒

© Sascha Feuchert, Charlotte Knobloch
www.indexoncensorship.org

*Translated by Ruth Ahmedzai Kemp*

**Sascha Feuchert** is director of Holocaust literature at the Justus Liebig University of Giessen and vice president of German PEN

**Charlotte Knobloch** is president of the Jewish Community of Munich and Upper Bavaria. She is former president of the Central Council of Jews in Germany and vice president of the World Jewish Congress and the European Jewish Congress

ABOVE: A Belarussian officer during pre-term voting at a polling station in Minsk, Belarus, in the last elections

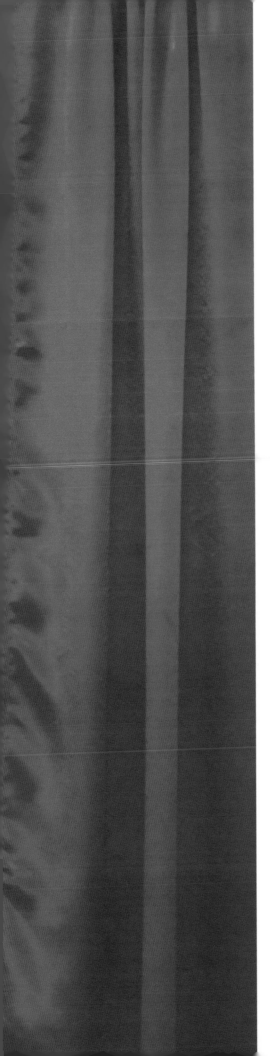

**CULTURE**

In this section

# Political framing

43(3): 124/127 | DOI: 10.1177/0306422014548148

**Kaya Genc** talks to radical Turkish artist and filmmaker Kutluğ Ataman about facing censorship and torture, and also about his controversial moderating role during the Gezi Park demonstrations

**W**HEN TURKISH CONTEMPORARY artist Kutluğ Ataman was 17 years old, plainclothes policemen visited him at home in Istanbul. Before taking him to a police station, where they would torture him, they made sure to collect the Super 8 films, stills and slides he had meticulously shot the previous year.

"My collection probably still exists in some dark corner in a storage room in a military facility, where they bring those kinds of things," Ataman told Index in the living room of his Istanbul apartment.

The apartment, which has a stunning view of the Bosphorus, has long been home to Turkey's most controversial contemporary artist and has served as a hub for the leading curators and artists of Turkey's burgeoning art scene. It was from here that Ataman watched thousands of protestors travelling to the quay in Karaköy in ferries, before they marched to Taksim, to join last year's protests.

Ataman is a devoted socialist and activist. In the months preceding the 1980 military coup which led to the ruthless dictator Kenan Evren taking over, Ataman was physically tortured and sent to a military hospital where he "was retrained to become a Turkish nationalist". He described how he was forced to recite the now defunct national oath during his imprisonment.

A few days before our interview, Evren was finally sentenced to life imprisonment following a trial in a criminal court, some 34 years after taking the reins of the country from democratically elected politicians. For Ataman the wounds of Evren's coup, which changed his life forever, are still fresh. He sees a parallel between the atmosphere of 1980 and the outpouring of energy during last year's demonstrations.

"On the one side there is this culture which says the state can do whatever it likes. On the other side, there are people who are so much oppressed that they just enjoy going to the streets to shout 'Enough!' I kind of understand that."

In the post-coup days, public expressions of dissent like organising public meetings or publishing publications critical of the official ideology, were strictly prohibited. In order to save him, Ataman's family bribed state officials to let him leave the country. "I didn't really have a say in my future because I was the guilty one bringing all this unhappiness on my family," he recounted. His parents told him to go as far as possible. So he went to the USA and graduated from the University of California, Los Angeles with a Master's degree in fine arts in 1988.

While he was there he continued to be involved in campaigning. "I had been heavily involved in the gay rights movement. It was the times of the Aids crisis and I was part of an activist group called Act Up. I was able to join all their political meetings and

ABOVE: Turkish artist Kutluğ Ataman at his exhibit for the 18th Istanbul Theatre Festival

was involved in extremely creative acts of discontent. I got into film-making and helped organise gay film festivals. Having done all of that, when I came back to Turkey, it was just normal for me to continue being the person I had become in the States."

He returned to his homeland in 1994, at the age of 33. In the 20 years that followed, his films and installations have brought him fame as well as notoriety. Ataman's first film, The Serpent's Tale, was a gothic story, based in Istanbul. His 1999 film, Lola and Billy the Kid, about a 17-year-old Turk's discovery of his homosexuality while living in Germany, won the Special Jury Prize at the Berlin International Film Festival (Berlinale). For his next project, Ataman adapted feminist Turkish author Perihan Mağden's novel Two Girls, and cast Hülya Avşar, the leading Turkish film star, in an important role. In 2009 he directed The Journey to the Moon, a mockumentary about an imaginary journey to the moon from a Turkish mosque in 1950s Erzincan. Screened at the BFI 53rd London Film Festival, the film featured real interviews about its imaginary subject matter with Turkey's leading intellectuals.

"I didn't have any problem with authorities upon my arrival in Turkey," Ataman said. "And yet people were always telling me: 'Oh you are so courageous, you are so great.' I never understood that. Yes, I had made the first openly gay film in Turkey, I was outspoken against seeing Atatürk statues

## Ataman was physically tortured and sent to a military hospital where he "was retrained to become a Turkish nationalist"

everywhere, I was really critical of the state ideology… but I never really understood why people always called me courageous. I felt that freedom to express myself was already there."

Four years into his new Turkish existence, things took a different turn. In 1997, the military attempted to engineer social and political life through the so-called 28 February post-modern coup.

"I learned about what had gone on during the post-modern coup later and I →

was scared," Ataman said. "At the time I was working on a video called Women Who Wear Wigs."

In the film a cancer survivor, a Muslim activist, a transsexual and a revolutionary, who all wear wigs for different reasons, tell their personal stories of how they have been affected by state ideology. "Had I known what I know today about what had been going on in that period, perhaps I would be scared to film it."

Ataman had made his entry into the art world in the year of the post-modern coup, with his documentary film about Semiha Berksoy, the famous Turkish opera diva. In Semiha B. Unplugged, the iconic singer talks to the camera continuously for eight hours. Following this film's success, Ataman

## During Gezi Park he argued that the protests had been hijacked by ultra-nationalists, and warned against a return to darker times

redefined himself as a video artist and participated in the 48th Venice Biennale with Women Who Wear Wigs.

"I was in the beginning of my career. With all their manipulations the military could have easily destroyed it, had they chosen to," he said. "Maybe today it would make news abroad but back then I had completely no shell, nothing to protect me. I had beginners' luck. I always felt that there were pockets of freedom back then. There were other areas you knew not to be so free. One of those pockets of freedom for us was the Istanbul Biennal. I always made sure that I created my most controversial works during the Biennal. I thought that if they wanted to do something they were not going to do it in front of the Europeans and foreigners."

In 2011 Ataman exhibited the health certificate he was issued by a Turkish Military Hospital about his "military status" and which showed his "unsuitability" for the army. It reads: "Self-care: good. Disposition: calm. Sociability: respectful. Speech: effeminate. Tone of voice: effeminate... Fails to show interest in women, shows interest in men."

"When I made my first application to the ministry of culture to get backing for a film project, some people from the film industry said 'Oh, he is a homosexual, he is not good for our country,' blah blah," said Ataman. "Professional people badmouthed me. They were horrible. They made sure that I didn't get any backing from the ministry. Those kinds of things I learned from the press, with everyone else."

During the noughties, Ataman argued that the expansion of the art scene and more funding for artists would result in more freedoms. "The market expanded but sometimes it hit no-go areas. For example, some Marmara University professors wanted to sue me because of my work in the Biennial. A lot of westerners automatically assume that this kind of censorship and oppression comes from Islamists. Personally, I never had that kind of censorship from them. But obviously, that doesn't mean that this kind of censorship doesn't exist. It's just that I personally never had it."

Ataman's international prestige increased with new video installations, Mesopotamian Dramaturges and Küba, which were screened in prestigious galleries, including The Serpentine in London and the Museum of Contemporary Art in Sydney. In 2003 UK newspaper The Observer picked Ataman as the best and brightest artist of the year.

But 11 years after being named a young bright artist, Ataman seems bored with the machinations of the art world, and says he wants to go back to making films. Warning against a new system of censorship, one that is created by financiers and capitalists who control the art world with cunning new methods, Ataman said: "Their methods of control are more dangerous to me than the crude state control of my youth. What happened then was that the state came, took your work and burnt it. It was all factual: you could prove it, but in the new liberal system the censorship is done in a much more efficient way. They make it so that the channels of production are cut from the very source. They control you with financing. Market economy, basically." In short, he has become a critic of the liberal market economy which he once believed would save the art world.

During last year's Gezi protests, Ataman was invited to become a member of a conciliatory committee, where a group of artists, intellectuals and actors attempted to negotiate a peace between protestors and the government. On national TV he argued that the protests were hijacked by ultra-nationalists, and warned against a return to darker times. Ataman's words created outrage among protestors, who accused him of selling out to the system.

"When you see people getting killed on the streets, I say: 'get the fuck out of here'," Ataman said. "I am not going to support you any more... People are getting killed, so go home, sit down. I get angry with both sides." He complained about the polarising discourse of the last year, which he said "united the whites and blacks who ended up attacking the people in the centre", the grey area where he sees himself, and where "people have the debate". He went on: "The fascists of the left and the right, they want to destroy the real workers, which is the position I occupy." Ataman's stance, and his support of it through his Twitter account, resulted in a kind of excommunication from the art world, which was united in its support for the protests.

"I was already switching from the art world back to my film-making. So it was a welcome break from the self-replicating art world. Sometimes the universe works in very amazing ways. Just look at the state of the art world since Gezi, since I have been out. Nothing is happening. The bubble has collapsed. The last Biennial was [dubbed] the worst Biennial ever. How can you come up with a Biennial like this after Gezi? It was the biggest betrayal."

Ataman has come full circle to his film-making. He was back this February at the Berlinale premiering his new film, Lamb, about village life in one of Turkey's poorest communities. The film will also be shown at the 58th BFI London Film Festival, which runs from 8 to 19 October this month.

"I have done what can be done in Turkey," Ataman said. "I had shows in the Istanbul Modern, Sabancı and Arter. There is nothing else to do here. Even if I become the toast of town it doesn't matter because I have done everything. I don't have any immediate plans for this country. I am just a tourist again." ☒

© Kaya Genç
www.indexoncensorship.org

**Kaya Genç** is a novelist and is Index on Censorship's contributing editor, based in Turkey. He was named as one of Turkish literature's top 20 writers under 40. He tweets @kayagenc

# Action drama

43(3): 128/131 | DOI: 10.1177/0306422014547483

Belarus Free Theatre is preparing for its 10th birthday and the Belarusian elections. The company's co-founder and artistic director, Natalia Kaliada, talks to **Julia Farrington** about her fears for the future

**N**ATALIA KALIADA IS unequivocal. The result of the 2015 election in Belarus is a foregone conclusion, even before the date of the election has been set.

"The day after the election, the electoral committee will make an announcement that Aleksandr Lukashenko has received 84 per cent of the vote. Many political activists will be jailed. Europe and the USA will not recognise the result of the election, but neither will they put any pressure on Lukashenko to change it."

The only wild card is the role Russia will play, she argues. "If Russia decides to invade Belarus then that would be a totally new development," she said. "Otherwise there will be no surprises from Lukashenko." Her cynicism is not surprising given not one of the elections held in Belarus since 1994 has been recognised by the OSCE as free and fair.

Right now, the BFT is preparing a series of dramatic actions to draw attention to the lack of freedom, and the upcoming elections, in the authoritarian state. These will include "solidarity parties" around Europe, working particularly with young people to expand knowledge about Belarus, and to illustrate what restrictions exist in the country. They are looking at staging events inside and around telephone boxes, which are similar in size to prison cells people are held in by Lukashenko.

Kaliada has done everything in her power to campaign for democracy in her country. This tireless commitment to raising awareness of human rights and political abuses has taken her and the company's co-founder, her husband Nikolai Khalezin, around the world speaking at the highest level to politicians in the UK, USA and across the EU.

Asked how different the upcoming election was to 2010, when Lukashenko returned to power for a fourth term with 80 per cent of the vote, she said: "The difference was that five years ago there was hope. Now, there is no hope. The opposition leaders are either political prisoners or ex-political prisoners, living in exile with no political rights in Belarus."

Lukashenko's destruction of the opposition started the day after the last election in 2010, when 30,000 people came into the main square in Minsk to protest the result. Hundreds of demonstrators, including six out of the nine opposition leaders, were arrested, and many of them brutally beaten. Natalia was also arrested. Nikolai went into hiding. The KGB were searching for supporters of the opposition. Kaliada worries that "next year it won't be a special division of police who will crack down on peaceful demonstration, but tanks".

Kaliadia describes how she was held for 20 hours in horrendous conditions with

ABOVE: Members of the Belarus Free Theatre, including co-founders Natalia Kaliada and her husband Nikolai Khalezin (centre), who fled Belarus after being held as political prisoners

Credit: Michiel van Nieuwkerk

no access to toilet facilities and no water. Guards threatened to rape her with a chair leg. As soon as she was released, she and her family were smuggled by friends in a car to Moscow before flying to the USA. They didn't know then that they would not be able to return. In April 2011, they flew to London where they claimed asylum. All this time they were campaigning for the release of political prisoners.

Later that year, Index arranged a meeting between them and the UK's deputy prime minister, Nick Clegg. "The next day our parents' apartments were raided by the KGB and our relatives were horribly beaten. My father-in-law died of a heart attack after one of these raids. This was the saddest moment of our exile," said Kaliada.

Since then Kaliada and her family and two other company members, including fellow artistic director Vladimir Shcherban, have made their home in London, and the theatre has become an associate company at the Young Vic. The majority of the company, 29 actors and students, remain in Belarus, where the company has always been underground. They perform where they can, in friends' apartments, in nightclubs before →

→ they open, in works' canteens after they close, in the forest, in small villages. She said: "We are just one company with two completely different realities – one part of the company in exile, and the other underground."

But, as the election year approaches Kaliada is in no doubt that the situation is getting worse. "The arrests, the interrogations have intensified," she said. "They have normalised. They used to happen two or three times a year, now it is every month. Last year we lost our venue, a small private house in the suburbs where we had rehearsed and performed for six years. The authorities threatened that they would knock the house down, so the owner had no choice but to ask us to leave.

## In Belarus, the audience risks arrest by attending the event, just as much as the company by performing

"Now they threaten people who offer us alternative spaces to rehearse or perform – threaten to take away their business licence, or threaten their children. So they cannot let us use it for long and we have to move on. This is a huge burden, also financially."

Next year, Belarus Free Theatre will celebrate its 10th birthday. When they started out, they never anticipated that the company would have this dual identity. They have continued to adapt, while remaining as connected as possible to their roots, rehearsing every day on Skype, teaching their students, coming up with new ideas. Each new show in London is live-streamed to their audiences in Belarus, including after-show discussions. Their company members travel to the UK to perform and tour, and to run workshops around the UK and internationally.

Meanwhile, their experience of producing and marketing shows in the UK has led to very different restrictions. Kaliada explained that it was now economics that dictated what she and the company could say and do.

She said: "When I was teaching our students underground in Belarus, I told them that if you go to a free society, you will get money from specific trusts and foundations only if you fit into their marketing strategy."

In Belarus, there is no right to freedom of assembly or freedom of expression. In Belarus, the audience risks arrest by attending the event, just as much as the company by performing. Just getting to see the show is a challenge – a text message directs them to a clandestine destination. Sometimes a wedding party is used as a front so they can perform their shows.

Belarus Free Theatre's core audience around the world is young – people aged 20 to 30, who find out about the shows on Facebook, Twitter and through word of mouth. Last year, they ran a campaign called Give a Body Back, alongside their show Trash Cuisine. The campaign was about capital punishment, based on stories members of the company had collected from all over the world. It centred on the call for the bodies of executed prisoners to be returned to their families in Belarus. They invited their audience to join their actors at three different places in London – Parliament Square, Trafalgar Square and Piccadilly Circus. They then asked people to get into body bags and stay still for one hour in protest.

"The entire staff of Oberon Books joined us," said Kaladia. "They closed the office for the day. It is really beautiful to develop such relations with an audience when it's clear that there is no need for us to be divided into the audience and the company, but we are just all together."

In spite of a deep-seated fatigue with realpolitik (conveyed in the title of their ongoing series of political actions to spotlight injustice, Fuck Real Politik), Natalia sees their campaigning in the political arena as crucial.

She anticipates that next year will bring urgent challenges on this front.

"Of course there will be arrests around the election," she said. "The EU will not react to arrests, we know that. It is horrible knowing that no-one does anything when people are arrested. But maybe we can lobby EU politicians to stop political prisoners from being tortured."

Would she ever consider being a politician herself if the political system changed in Belarus? "No, no, no! We need to have the right to criticise politicians always," she said. "Because there will always be things to criticise even if democracy comes to Belarus." ☒

© Julia Farrington
www.indexoncensorship.org

**Julia Farrington** is Index on Censorship's arts associate, head of campaigns at the Belarus Free Theatre and convener of the Index Arts Freedom Wales conference in October

# Casting away

43(3): 132/144 | DOI: 10.1177/0306422014549150

Playwright **Ariel Dorfman** says that many obsessions, literary, biographical and political, converge in his new short story Casting Away, published here for the first time

**WRITER AND HUMAN** rights activist Ariel Dorfman published the first English-language version of his play Death and the Maiden in Index On Censorship magazine in the 1990s, when democracy had just returned to Chile after the 1973 coup.

His latest short story, Casting Away, is set inside the office of a casting director as someone, who is presumably an actor, prepares to resign from a long-standing role, and has resonances with the questions we ask ourselves about life and death.

## Add a dash of fascination with the relationship between power and literature – literature as power of the imagination, power in society and politics as a way in which those in authority censor and repress

The author, whose work has been translated into more than 50 languages, said: "I have always felt, since childhood, that someone is inhabiting me, that I am merely acting out a script engineered by others, that the control I believe I exercise over my life – that all of us believe we exercise over our own lives – is not more than an illusion. Couple that with my long-standing interest in the mass media – comic and film, soap operas and popular culture – as a major, often insidious, force that shapes our contemporary consciousness, and you have a glimpse into the origins of this short story. And, for good measure, add a dash of fascination with the relationship between power and literature – literature as power of the imagination, power in society and politics as a way in which those in authority censor and repress and manipulate that imagination – and the brew is complete."

Dorfman, whose recently published memoir Feeding on Dreams charts his years of exile after Pinochet's coup, said: "As in so many of my works, here I also wish to discover those acts of love and companionship, those words of hope and small glories, that we humans are able to create and nurse and transmit despite all the alienating commands and commanders of the universe. Although the narrator is limited (as we the readers are) by what he knows about his condition, the fine print that defines his existence, the fine print of our ultimate contract with death and destiny that we never read until it is too late; in spite of all this, I trust that there stirs in my nameless protagonist a redemption that transcends his life as spectacle, a love for one person above all that offers consolation and perhaps salvation, I trust that the reader may be as moved as I was by his dilemma, his dilemma and ours."

## Casting Away

**"I CAN'T GO ON,"** I say. "Not one more day, not one more episode, not a whole season, that's the truth. I'm all worn out."

The Casting Director doesn't look up from the head shot she's examining. She turns it this way, that way, peers at a slight blemish on the cheek of her subject's face (unrecognisable no matter how much I try to find a resemblance to someone I know), lays the picture in a pile to her right, picks up another one, nods with pursed lips and places this one, just as unfamiliar to me, in a larger, separate group of photos. Then she reaches out her long hand with those pink fingernails, selects a piece of paper from a neat bunch at her side and begins to read, making a point of not even slanting her eyes towards me.

I wondered if this is a tactic she always uses, a strategy of silence perfected in the decades since I'd last visited her, last come to her long ago, a whole lifetime ago, in fact. On that occasion I was suitably impressed but I'm even more impressed now, overwhelmed perhaps is the appropriate word, left almost speechless.

I'd been told – the receptionist warned me while I cooled my heels out in the waiting area, but he was only repeating what I had already heard through the grapevine – that she didn't seem to age, *be prepared to be surprised*, but still, I was startled when I came through the door and sat down in front of her, she gestured to the armchair without bothering to even glance in my direction, it was puzzling that she looks exactly like the first and only time we met, over 60 years

ABOVE: Playwright and human rights activist Ariel Dorfman

back. As if, while I was labouring away for decades, working my character to the bone, while time frayed him and me down, not a minute, not even a second, had passed for her. She remained here, in the same colossal office I recalled – that hadn't changed either, cavernous enough to accommodate an army of Casting Directors rather than just one, she had adamantly lingered here, making sure each individual in each show she commandeered got the perfect match, obtained the utmost attention.

→

→ Maybe it's that work ethic which keeps her perpetually young. Or maybe my memory is playing tricks with me and this wasn't the same Casting Director, in spite of what the receptionist had confided. Maybe it was the daughter of the woman who way back then had discussed my options with me, gone through potential vacancies and available candidates for my services, explained exhaustively the terms and conditions of the contract. Her daughter? More likely her granddaughter, the spitting image. But no, that wasn't possible. It was her,

## Her eyes keep reading the piece of paper as if it were a sacred text or a memo from the past as to what to do next

exactly, precisely, identically her, the image of those irrevocable lips had been burnt into my retina like a sun that never sets, it was her, untouched by the wheel of fortune or the dust of time, unaffected by sorrow or frustration or small coups of artistic achievement, as immaculate as a deity in a temple.

I had scoffed at the admonitions of the others in the waiting area, at what the receptionist had told me was his experience. *Prepare to be surprised*, he had said, *but no matter how astonished you may be*, the others had added, *don't broach the subject with her, act as if it's the most natural thing in the world that she comes to work every morning – she's always here, maybe she doesn't even go home, but the point is that she continues to dress in the same drab colours,*

*wears the same fashions in vogue a century ago or more. Try to stay in her good graces,* that's what they recommended, *so she'll cast around for a new job soon and not leave you dangling for who knows how long.* Right! No Casting Director, and especially not this one, likes to be subjected to scrutiny or doubt. Their unquestioned infallibility lends them authority – comforting for those of us engaged in this precarious profession of embodiment, trusting that her execution is impeccable, can be relied on to always act in the best interests of both performer and character and, of course, making sure that the all-powerful spectator is entertained, tunes in again and again.

So I have tried to be on my best behavior and not point out any apparent anomalies, did not even allude to the fact that this was the second time we met. Just stated my decision, my words "I can't go on, I'm all worn out", hovering in the grey light filtering from the shuttered windows above, as if this office had not been cleaned for millennia, tiny mites dancing in the thick murk of the air that she and I are both breathing, though she seems more like a statue, immobile now except for her eyes that keep reading that piece of paper as if it were a sacred text or a memo from the past as to what to do next, how she should answer requests such as mine.

Not as if there's that much to it, really.

She has to honour the contract. Once a player comes in, states unequivocally that he or she needs to retire, not one more day, not one more episode, not a whole season, that was it. Negotiations have to start, it's no longer a matter of if and whether, but when and how. The Casting Director would do her legendary best to persuade me to stay on for a while, gauge how truly weary and bored and desperate I am, try to entice me with the promise of a couple of bravura moments that were being readied exclusively for me, if I reconsidered, that is. Just for a while. She knows, as I did when I accepted this assignment, that nobody keeps a job like this forever, forever is not a word people like her ever use. But she's adept, according to rumours, at convincing the most recalcitrant participants to prolong their commitment, at least until the Producers come up with a plausible explanation for my sudden departure, a satisfying ending for the audience out there, for the ratings god that is the only one who really matters.

"You can't say you didn't know."

I hear my voice as if it didn't belong to me, as if somebody was mouthing me in voice over. It pipes up out of me irrepressibly, making me ignore the advice, everybody else's experience, that one should let the Casting Director answer before any further explanations or excuses, make her feel the uncomfortable weight of this protracted immobility. *Let her listen to the ticking clock. It's ticking more for her than for you, she's the one who needs to find a solution.* Time is on my side, all I need to do, ultimately, is not show up, one day simply call in sick – though nobody has ever dared to do so, nobody has had the guts to simply withdraw and leave the other players and their characters in the lurch. We'd be justified, given the hours we put in, only resting when our protagonists sleep, and even then bothered by dreams or nightmares.

It speaks well of me, earns me points, not to have ever pretended I had to flu, no unilateral pressure applied on my part, adamantly opposed to strikes or collective action as a way of bettering our working conditions, always the most considerate and deferential of players, always played by the rules.

I press the point.

"I've always played by the rules," I say. And add, I can't help myself, my motor mouth is running away from me, just as it always does for the character I embody: "It's not as if I didn't give you fair warning. I asked for this little conversation of ours months ago. You're busy, I respect that. Everyone respects that. And don't think I don't appreciate what you've done for me. It's been

## Nobody has had the guts to simply withdraw and leave the other players and their characters in the lurch

a good run. You promised me a juicy role – those were the very words you used, if I'm not mistaken – and I have no complaints, I mean you could have insisted with any number of minor, terminal, secondary bit parts in Godforsaken lands forgotten by mapmakers, offered them up interminably until you forced me to submit. And the scenes! I can't deny I've had some stellar scenes."

I smile, try to make it radiant, remind her that critics have raved about my smile, remind her and anyone who happens to be eavesdropping on this one-way conversation that my presence in the show has driven →

→ up the viewings, so it is rumoured, with the only watcher that really matters, the owner of the studio, the big boss. Better not to mention that, *don't ever appear boastful*, my Agent had driven home the advice all those decades ago. Right! No bragging, no preening. Let them draw their own conclusions, give them a chance to give you your very own show if they feel so inclined, shine the spotlight on you, syndication, run-offs, the works.

I wait. The Casting Director doesn't blink, concentrates on her infernal piece of paper. Wait her out, wait her out. I can't, I just can't. I need this over and done with, I need closure.

## She has spies and eyes everywhere, everything recorded and registered for posterity

"Stellar scenes, but intense. But maybe too intense, so intense, so deeply embodied, that they've tired me out, I've been going at it day in, day out, for-"

I stop. I sound as if I'm complaining. And I'm not, Just grateful. Maybe I should make sure she understands just how grateful I am for the opportunity, especially for the extraordinary woman they gave for me to love over so many episodes, how grateful I – but she's heard the same litany a million times, there's nothing she hasn't heard, no praise she hasn't soaked up, no protests left unattended, she doesn't need to listen to a poor soul like me blabbing relentlessly to guess why.

And besides, she has spies and eyes everywhere, everything recorded and registered for posterity, the piece of paper she's reading now must be one of the daily, perhaps hourly, reports she receives, probably about me, an instant evaluation of my latest performance, my recent lack of enthusiasm for the role, mistakes I may have lapsed into, tiny telltale signs that something is amiss, minor squabbles with the costume designer and the props manager, and that soon enough I'd be requesting a meeting with her. She could well even now have a solution in hand, have arranged for a replacement while I reconsidered, organise my character's disappearance from the screen for a few months, simulate a fake trip overseas, give me time to change my mind and return to the show invigorated, an incident that would not overly disturb the flow of events. Anyone who makes it all the way to Casting Director has proven her worth a thousand times over, has faced ultimatums far more abrupt than mine, she must have already devised a plan, negotiated with the team of script writers, the decorators in charge of the set, contacted the legal department. This meeting of ours is a mere formality, making public and official what everybody has surely been gossiping about privately: one more player who's all worn out.

I'm not the only one.

Thus far, except for my intermittent chatter, it has been quiet in here. Plush carpeting drowns out all noise, even the sound I make each time I lean forward, shift my armchair to draw closer to her, emphasise a point. But now, from nearby, what must be the

ABOVE: A film studio –"The Casting Director must have devised a plan, negotiated with the writers, the decorators in charge of the set"

Credit: Shutterstock/Igor Terekhov igor

next room where another Casting Director is receiving her protégé, perhaps delivering some bad news, a termination slip, notice that a show has been cancelled, a typhoon or an earthquake or a bomb or a famine has wiped out an entire cast – or is about to. Or maybe something less catastrophic, more personal: some character's darling son or brother is slated to die in the next episode – as if I don't know what that means, though I was given no advance warning about my love, I would have sobbed like that, I did so on screen many times, with dreadful precision, played the part to the hilt, I would also have punctuated this stillness with cries if I had been trawled in to be hit with horrible reports of sorrow, would have heard rise within me howls of despair.

The Casting Director grimaces. Without lifting her eyes, her index finger presses a yellow button on the desk. The sound ceases as suddenly as it began, allows her to concentrate again on her piece of paper, finish perusing it. She sighs again, grabs a pen – seems to snatch it out of thin air –, signs at the bottom, with a flourish meant to stress her decisiveness. Also as if from nowhere, the receptionist emerges, reverently collects the piece of paper, winks at me with encouragement as he turns to leave, gives me the thumbs up as he disappears out the door.

## Some character's darling son or brother is slated to die in the next episode – as if I don't know what that means

So it isn't a report about me that the Casting Director has been reading, it doesn't concern me or this meeting. Unless it was an order she was handing out, her consent to my petition before I've even formulated it, unless she's been so far-sighted that when, over a year ago, I'd asked for this interview, she →

→ had understood so completely, was so up to date about my determination, knew it before I did, was so clear as to what would transpire today that she had prepared the paperwork and thus will now simply declare to me: "Right, it's done, thanks for the coming in, we'll be in touch as soon as we have another proposal for you, something juicy is sure to open up soon, hope you won't be so fussy next time around."

She doesn't say anything of the sort. She just reaches for a compact sheaf of papers. This one is definitely not a report. I catch a glimpse of clauses and items, addenda and fine print: a contract! It may take her a while to wade through all that. Maybe it's my final settlement or the deal I signed so long ago, maybe she's reviewing it now to make sure I'm not in breach of terms and conditions as originally stipulated.

## The Casting Director either admires me for my stubbornness or resents how I resisted her overtures

I rack my brains but have trouble recalling any of that, especially the fine print, I'm ashamed to admit it.

Because my Agent, while escorting me to the waiting room all those years ago, had offered two pieces of advice.

First: don't accept that woman's initial offer, or the second or third one, no matter how succulent the role may seem, how hard she tries to sell you the goods. She'll want to test you, unload some minor character that nobody else wants.

And I had listened to him earnestly, I was so young back then, so inexperienced. It was crucial to mind my custodian's caveats, select well who I was to spend my next decades with – or my next few hours, if I wasn't careful, if I made a flawed choice. I might not have a chance to perfect my art and hone my talents, run the gamut of emotions, inhabit my subject's dilemmas to the hilt, not really practice for an even more significant role next time around, climb the ladder of success, the spotlight, the spotlight we all desire so much until it is too late and we realise that that's not what matters. Watch out, my Agent had admonished: too many aspirants find themselves short-changed, dead-ended, relegated to a secondary position at the end of season one, outshone by some other performer. Until you sign on the dotted line, you are in control. Be picky, my boy.

And she must now remember just how picky this boy was. The Casting Director either admires me for my stubbornness or resents how I resisted her overtures, at times irrationally (she offered me the role of a Prince, no less), precluded her first three proposals. So maybe that's why she's been so silent and unresponsive. She has it in for me, now she'll put forward some dull incarnation, someone who repeats the same forlorn sequence of events, day after day, she may have been nursing a grudge, planning to teach me a lesson all this time. Let's see who's picky now, boy.

But no, I'm letting my apprehensions run riot. She has a soft spot for me. She's used to first-time applicants rejecting the initial vacancies, she can't be oblivious to the tactics of all those Agents out there, the sort of guidance they give their clients and wards. Maybe they're even in agreement, each Agent and each Casting Director, negotiating ahead of time and behind our backs which role will be accepted, taking care to give players like me the illusion that we are in command.

At any rate, either because it was her plan all along or it was my ability to follow the Agent's strict instructions, it turned out fine for me. At the fourth attempt, the fourth time she dragged out photos, a pilot episode, a full dossier and a partial treatment, I was hooked. *Take your time,* she said, *we have all the time in the world. Better to be safe than sorry, we wouldn't want you to be unhappy or your protagonist to feel you weren't giving him your best shot.*

Unhappy? Not me. As soon as I saw the array of head shots and body shots, torso and fingerprints and those curved ears of his, the man I was going to embody and burrow into, the man I was going to research and rehearse and arouse, as soon as I caught a glimpse of his mischievous eyes and his freckled skin, as soon as I managed a whiff of how he smelled and the lushness of his voice even when he was wailing, his voice and his tongue so pink, well, I fell in love with him, how can I deny it? I vowed I would be his servant for as long as our mutual episodes lasted, his servant but also his master, also leading and persuading him to utter his lines with conviction. It has to be done subtly so he doesn't realise what or who is possessing him, so he succumbs to the mirage of free will, my Acting Coach

and Dialect Instructor and Make Up Lady, they all explained, he can't suspect that your shadow is inside him, that without you he'd be a zombie, as good as dead, that you're his mirror on the road, that there's a script written for him that pre-determines his whole life as a character, each nuance debated and approved by a committee, enforced by the director, we wouldn't want any rebellion or hesitancy to creep in and interfere with the performance. As long as you really like him, really understand what the man dreams and desires, are willing to fuse with him, entwine his fate and yours, all will be well.

So I said yes, entranced and proud that I had heeded the Agent when we stopped

# There's a script written for him that pre-determines his whole life as a character, each nuance approved by a committee

outside the Waiting Room and he urged me to refuse the first three roles, even if one of them is a Prince. And then he had another recommendation, a second and last recommendation, before saying goodbye. *I'm afraid my guardianship ends here, once you go through that door. No need to worry, I have vetted every contract, they're all pretty standard, you'll manage just fine on your own from now on. As long as you heed another piece of advice, the second one I mentioned. Read the fine-print, my boy. I may have missed something,* the Agent admitted, shamefacedly, *I may have misunderstood some obscure and convoluted* →

ABOVE: A stack of film scripts – "Scripts overflowed from each shelf, each episode with its own black binder and a date on it"

→ clause. *The fine print, that's where they screw you over, be careful.*

I took his first piece of advice about not giving in easily to the exhortations of the Casting Director, but was less willing to follow the Agent's counsel regarding the fine print.

The Casting Director had been a sweetheart – not like now, where she adamantly keeps examining page after page –, hadn't flinched when I turned down the first three candidates and had finally come up with – *a*

*marriage made in heaven,* she had chortled, and I thought I saw her open and close her left eye at me, though such familiarity was not be expected from such a highly placed executive, so I must have been hallucinating. But what counts is that she added: *yes, in heaven indeed, like all our collaborations, approved by those above us, those who infinitely know and care.*

So she had been clearly pleased when I had ardently embraced the character she displayed for me in all his glory, warts and all.

Which is why, when she extracted the contract from inside her desk back then and handed it to me after having made explicit the main terms, I received the bundle of papers and scanned them somewhat mechanically, feigning an interest I did not feel – already the consummate actor, trying out my wares on none other than the Casting Director, but to tell the truth I was fed up with so much legalese and ifs and buts and therefores. By then, the session had lasted who knows how many hours – or had we been cloistered in her office for days or weeks? – and I'd been anxious to get on with the job, filled with excitement at the prospect of an unspoiled life ahead, fresh as a baby about to be born, written and planned expressly – or so she had assured me, perhaps to entice me to accept the role, but she had declared something similar about the three previous ones I had rejected – expressly for me, she said, aware, of course, that I would not read the fine print, keen as I was to make the acquaintance of the character I'd henceforth be inhabiting, particularly eager to cross paths in the distant future episodes with his future wife, the love of my character's life, the woman who has made all this worthwhile for him and for me.

I had signed on the dotted line and had never seen the Casting Director again, had never needed to.

Until now. Until the unthinkable had happened.

All worn out.

Those words, I'd said those exact words out loud, just a while ago, but I hadn't explained the circumstances to her, to the Casting Director, did I really need to? Hasn't she been keeping tabs on me?

As if guessing my thoughts, the Casting Director turns to look at the wall behind her and lets her gaze slide over the cluster of scripts that overflow from each shelf, each episode with its own black binder and a date on it, shelves upon shelves, stretching upwards to a ceiling so far away I can hardly discern where it ends. And sideways too, the bookcases seem to extend endlessly left and right, irrevocably, in both directions.

I catch some of the dates and recognise them, each one has a personal meaning. These are my scripts, the interminable pages brimming with gestures and grimaces, headaches and joys written for me, for my character. For a moment I think this is an honor, that the Casting Director has taken the trouble to order that the full array of my existence and performances this time around be stacked up in her enormous office for this one interview. It must have taken an army of functionaries many days to transfer those binders from the vast vaults in which they have lain dormant, unvisited except by some assistant in charge of continuity and consistency, it must have taken an executive order to wrest these old scripts from some dank cellar – all that work so I can – I can what? Be reminded of the life I'm abandoning, abandoning my best friend in the world, the man I have incarnated, the brother I'm dooming to extinction.

It's a manoeuvre, emotional blackmail. My memories, that's what the Casting Director is taking such pains to display. She knows what I treasure most: the episode where my character and I met his future wife, almost lost the chance to ask her out on a date, fumbled that first lightening encounter, was

## It's a manoeuvre, emotional blackmail. My memories, that's what the Casting Director is taking such pains to display

consoled by a buddy at a bar, counselled not to let this moment pass. *Hey, man, she might be The One, heaven is always just around the corner but we keep passing it by without a second glance, without a second thought. Well, if I were you, my man, from the way you're describing her and your eyes are mooning all over, I'd say you should give her more than a second thought.*

What was his name? How could I have forgotten? It was there, that name, anyway, if I dare to stand up right now, break protocol and cross the room and leaf through those binders till I find the episode, I know the exact date. I can read through it right now, before my resignation is accepted, →

before I go off to my well-deserved rest, recover that major moment in my life. Read through it as I did when I prepped for the daily work routine, rehearsed the lines, primed myself to enact each movement of my character's body. Relive how I had managed to track the elusive girl down – the writers had been extremely clever, they had fed me the right, immaculate words to persuade that girl to go out on a – had it been a picnic, a movie, a dance, a hike, a dinner, a couple of drinks?

I've forgotten those details. How could I have forgotten those details?

A wave of nostalgia sweeps over me.

## I would carry her memory with me to whatever other job I was lucky enough to land, smuggle her with me into the future

If I could only sail back to that day, those nights, the first time I had made love with her and what she had whispered in my ear, secret stanzas that no one watching the show could have heard or guessed, not even the Big Boss or anyone else, words that only belonged to the two of us, words that were not in any of those binders or those cosmic shelves, her words for him, her words for me, that no hack writer had invented, that no Casting Director had appraised or approved, that no sound designer had captured with multiple microphones hidden under the pillows, words that I will take with me during my imminent retirement, the music of her milk and her breasts made into clandestine language

spoken so softly. The very words that I had just as quietly murmured to her – so quietly, again, that only she could perceive them as she lay on her deathbed, I had given them back to her as a farewell present, as a way of saying good-bye, another way of saying hello yet one more, one last time, so she would know that I remembered, that she might die but what I felt for her would never, could never, disappear, not in this world, not in the next one, that I would carry her memory with me to whatever other job I was lucky enough to land, smuggle her with me into the future.

That was our secret, our flaunting of the rules, our revenge for what the Producers had sprung on us: that accident, like a thunderbolt from above or a cesspool from below, and there it was, before we could even protest, grasp that there was something to protest about, before the professional who was performing her lines and her life could arrange a meeting to iron things out and arrange for a more prolonged and dignified exit, it was over. Or maybe she did, maybe she managed to get from them that last scene, managed to let me see her for that one last time, because she had been preparing those words for her exit and was not going to be cheated out of it.

I can't be certain that this was her plan. Contact between players outside the set is strictly forbidden and even more strictly enforced. All I really knew about the woman assigned the role of my wife was what we shared on the set, what had been written for her in the countless scripts hoarded on those shelves behind the Casting Director. What that performer did with her time when we weren't performing, that was none of my business, that was a different story, literally someone else's story, her story and not mine. Which made those buried, terminal words she had whispered to me off script after our first night of love all the more valuable, all the more valuable that I had returned them to her as she faded away in the arms of my character and my arms, sent her that hidden farewell message under the hospital lights and the studio lights and the lights of faraway constellations – a small sanctuary of intimate words that were not made for transmission or consumption or public spectacle, something mine, something yours, something only ours. Those words that gave me faith that my wife's departure from the world and from the show had been resolved by others, hope that she had not been the one to give up on me, she had not left me alone without putting up a fight.

And that had been the beginning of the end, nothing had been able to comfort me, no matter how many enticements the screenwriters cooked up to whet my appetite, to make me look forward to the next episode or a new season. She wasn't by my side and everything was empty.

That was when the idea began to form in my mind, the blasphemous notion that the moment might have arrived to pack it in, the future without her was meaningless, that's when I realised that all this time she had been the one to give me the energy to keep on performing, she was the one who had nurtured me, was my pillar of strength, and always had been, even before we had met, even before that friend whose name I can't recall told me not to let heaven escape

when it is just around the corner, even before she had whispered words to me that nobody had ever imagined, words only for me. Ever since I had caught a glimpse of her photo in the hands of the Casting Director as she explained my role, how there was this extraordinary woman who had already agreed to play my future wife, agreed, that is, if I also said yes, she had also been offered a glimpse of my head shot, it was love before first sight, way before first sight.

She was gone.

And what was I left with? More and more my character and I spent our time remembering the distant past, scenes from childhood

## All I really knew about the woman assigned the role of my wife was what we shared on the set, what had been written for her in the countless scripts

flashing back on the screen of the mind – tricks he and I had engaged in when he was a youngster, apples he had stolen from an orchard dappled with moonlight and another night he and I had spent on the grass and under the pines counting comets and distinguishing mythical figures in the sky, wondering if on those celestial bodies someone just like one of us, if somebody like the woman we were already anticipating, dreaming her as she dreamed me, was staring into the void, someone like her or like me wondering if this life, this universe, was nothing more than a simulacrum, a façade, a galactic spectacle mounted for the pleasure of some concealed god. →

→ Living in the past, looking backwards.

A sure sign that I was growing old, concerned with retaining what I would soon lose rather than with accumulating new experiences. Already saying goodbye to myself, to the character I had played my whole life, the mask of memories and desires he had tried on, already preparing for this interview with the Casting Director.

Would they allow me to carry those memories with me when I lapsed into the transitory retirement that was coming up, could I take some with me so I could spend time with each memory before dismissing it, before it was erased, obliterated to make space for whatever new role was being planned for me, a different life that would excite me all over again, use me to the hilt, push me to employ every resource in my repertoire, all the tricks and strategies I had learned during this run, what was rooted now in every fiber and gesture of my body. I know it's forbidden, somewhere in the fine print I never read, but she explained it to me, the Casting Director was quite explicit about this clause: you can't take anything from your old life into your new job.

Well, she's finished reading the contract or whatever it was that had required such urgent and concentrated attention, maybe she's been looking for that very item so she can show it to me in case I make an inquiry. But no. She sets the contract aside, slowly lifts her gaze to meet mine.

"I'm not giving up, not surrendering," I say, in the most amicable voice I can muster, so we can part on friendly terms. "It's just this role I've grown weary of. I'll accept another one. Once I've rested, I'll be glad to entertain other offers, something as juicy as this one."

She looks at me with her sad, eternal eyes.

And speaks for the first and last time.

"Who says there's another role? Who says a soul like yours gets another chance?"

I don't respond.

All I do is whisper some words to myself that she can't hear, that the Casting Director is straining to catch and capture. But she can't hear the words that the love of my life breathed into me like milk that night long ago, I have no other words to call my own, no other words to hold on to as I fade into the gathering dark. ☒

© Ariel Dorfman
www.indexoncensorship.org

**Ariel Dorfman** is a Chilean-American writer. He lives in Durham, North Carolina, in the US, where he teaches at Duke University. His latest book is the memoir Feeding on Dreams: Confessions of an Unrepentant Exile

# Index around the world

*by* **Alice Kirkland**

**INDEX NEWS**

43(3): 145/147 | DOI: 10.1177/0306422014548969

INDEX LAUNCHED ITS first interactive documentary in July, to show how Egyptian artists are tackling sexual harassment through theatre, street art, comic strips and rap music. Shout Art Loud – by Index's senior advocacy officer Melody Patry – uses a mix of video footage, interviews and illustrations to highlight a serious problem. In Egypt, 99% of women have experienced some form of sexual harassment, and 80% of females feel unsafe on the street. A new law criminalising sexual harassment was approved this summer, but assaults are still rife and Index remains in constant touch with artists working on the ground to continue highlighting the issue. You can watch the documentary on the website: www.indexoncensorship.org/shoutartloud

Just ahead of the 25th anniversary of the fall of the Berlin Wall, the summer edition of the Index on Censorship magazine was launched at the Goethe Institut in west London in July. Debating the extent of our freedom in modern Europe, speakers included playwright David Edgar; academic and writer Timothy Garton Ash; V&A museum director Martin Roth; Polish LGBT activist Tomasz Kitlinski; and journalists Kate Maltby and Sebastian Borger. Afterwards, audience members – including Index supporters, journalists and activists – carried on the discussion on the terrace.

In June, Index brought together five prominent journalists and activists from Russia, Turkey and Azerbaijan to address increasing threats to digital freedom. The discussion – which took place in Brussels – was hosted by Index's CEO Jodie Ginsberg, and sponsored by Google. The panel included: Andrei Soldatov, a Russian investigative journalist; Anton Nossik, blogger and founding editor-in-chief of several Russian news websites; Dr Yaman Akdeniz, founder and director of Cyber-Rights.org and professor of law at Istanbul Bilgi University; Amberin Zaman, Turkish correspondent for The Economist; and Azerbaijani blogger Arzu Geybulla. The main focus was what the EU should be doing to curb attacks and protect those under threat.

During the World Cup in Brazil, Index highlighted free expression concerns in the 32 participating countries by publishing statistics cards for each nation ahead of each game. Countries were awarded a score based on democracy, civil liberties, press freedom, net freedom and corruption. Those will poor tallies were handed a red or yellow card, with the four worst (Iran, Cameroon, Nigeria and Russia) forming Index's "group of death".

To support and develop Index's work with young people, a youth advisory board has been established and the first meeting was held – via Google Hangouts – in June. The eight members from around the world, who all applied through Index's website, will hold monthly discussions on free speech issues and will inform Index's future work. One of their roles includes coming up with questions for the Draw the Line debates, where each month a new freedom of expression →

ABOVE: Nigerian human rights lawyer Rommy Mom visiting the Index on Censorship office

→ question is posed to the public, who are encouraged to have their say via social media, offline workshops and by contributing themed content to the Index Young

# What should the EU be doing to curb attacks on digital freedom and protect those under threat?

Writers' Programme. Questions so far have included: "Can art or journalism ever be terrorism?" and "Should free speech offending countries be excluded from global sports tournaments?"

In May, the Court of Justice of the European Union ruled that individuals had "a right to be forgotten" online and search engines needed to respond to citizens' requests to take down information deemed out of date, irrelevant or excessive. Index's CEO Jodie Ginsberg was invited on to TV and radio shows, including the BBC and Channel 4 News. She argued that a regulatory framework and appeals process are needed to ensure that private corporations do not become the arbiters of public information.

Index was privileged to have a visit from the first editor of Index on Censorship, Michael Scammell, this spring. It was fascinating to hear more about the early years of the organisation. The contribution of Nadine Gordimer, the Nobel Prize-winning author and Index patron who died in July, was acknowledged in a collection of her writing for the magazine, which was collated on the website of our publisher, Sage. Index is very grateful for her support and that of former board member Dan Jacobson, another one of South Africa's leading novelists, who died in June.

Since the 2014 Index awards, nominees and winners have also been hard at work. Arts nominee Meltem Arikan has finished writing the script to her new play Sheep Republic, while fellow playwright and nominee Lucien Bourjeily has also been working on a new play, the sequel to Will It Pass Or Not?, which was banned in Lebanon. Digital activism award winner Shubhranshu Choudhary has been busy implementing a new project in rural India for CGNet Swara, using arts and puppetry to teach locals how to report news through their mobile phones. Nigerian lawyer Rommy Mom, who visited the Index offices in May to speak about the consequences of the country's Same Sex Marriage Prohibition Act, which has seen Nigerians imprisoned and murdered for being gay; he continues to offer support to those in the country who suffer human rights violations. David Cecil, who was deported from Uganda after staging what was deemed a "pro-gay" play in the country, is planning to open film schools in several African countries, including Tunisia, and hopes to move back to Africa soon. As we went to press, the winner of Index's journalism award Azadliq – one of the few remaining independent media outlets in Azerbaijan – has been forced to suspend publication due to a financial crisis.

Preparations are already under way for the next awards ceremony in March 2015, so look out for the nomination form on Index's website from 13 October. Please think about nominating organisations and individuals who are doing great work, often against the odds, to fight for freedom of expression. ☒

© Index on Censorship
www.indexoncensorship.org

**Alice Kirkland** is an editorial assistant at Index on Censorship

# From the factory floor

**END NOTE**

43(3): 148/149 | DOI: 10.1177/0306422014548632

There's no excuse for not knowing the working conditions behind a cheap shirt, now that workers can use technology to share details from their factory, says **Vicky Baker**

**"F**ORCED TO WORK** exhausting hours," read the hand-stitched label found in a cheap Primark dress in Wales in June. Taken as a cry for help from the factory floor, the story ran in many leading news outlets before being debunked as a hoax. The retailer's internal investigation concluded that the two near-identical labels found in the Swansea store were in items of clothing made thousands of miles apart: one in Romania, the other in India.

Yet hoax or not, the initial outcry says it all. In our hyper-connected world, it still seemed plausible that voiceless workers could be smuggling out news of their working conditions, like an SOS.

"Disconnection is the biggest problem. Consumers are disconnected from the origins of the products, and so are the companies," says Heather Franzese, director and co-founder of Good World Solutions, a company that has been working to bridge the gap by allowing workers to report anonymously on their conditions via their mobile phones.

The company first trialled the platform at a sweater factory in Peru in 2009, using an SMS-based system so users could send text messages about their working life and needs.

Later, the platform – named Labour Link – became voice-based, with pre-recorded audio prompts to ensure illiterate users weren't overlooked. The retailers that sign up then pick up the tab – as they should – so the workers can use the service for free.

Now working in 13 countries, including China and Bangladesh, Good World Solutions has surveyed 125,000 workers in its first four years. It has found workers have had confidence to divulge sensitive information, including cases of sexual harassment and child labour. The company – which has clients that include Marks & Spencer and, since 2013, Primark – has also moved from tailor-making questions to adopting a standardised format, so data can be compared. As a result, instead of just driving down prices and encouraging consumers to take an increasingly throwaway attitude to fashion, companies could also be driving up standards and creating new benchmarks.

Such action would certainly be more admirable than walking away. After a factory that made Disney apparel among other goods burnt down in Bangladesh in 2012, killing 112, the Walt Disney Company put the whole country on its blacklist. Now none of its products can be made there. The factory workers didn't have an exit; the big company did.

But Franzese says the collapse of the Bangladesh's Rana Plaza factory, which killed 1,129 garment workers in April 2013 and led to an outcry against foreign brands contracting negligent employers, was a turning point. "We get companies coming to us saying, 'We want to be more transparent'. Transparency is the future now," says Franzese. Also, unlike traditional social audits done onsite with a clipboard over a short period, Labour Link's communication channel can stay open and changes can be monitored over time.

Companies worldwide are also starting to experiment with what has been named "wearable technology", meaning devices such as glasses, armbands and watches that monitor your movements, heart rate, sleep patterns. ABI Research predicts 90m wearable devices will be shipped this year; most are designed for fashion or fitness, but there is growing interest in their use within the workplace. Further down the line we might see Google Glass, or a cheaper version, on the factory floor, bringing increased transparency, but also concerns over the boundaries in surveillance.

Phoebe Moore, a senior international relations lecturer at the University of Middlesex London, is researching a book about self-tracking and wearable technology. She says: "When companies start comparing your output against your colleagues, this is where the darker side comes in. Then it becomes more explicitly about productivity, rather than workers' wellbeing. On one side of this debate, you have surveillance and control; on the other, a real potential for work satisfaction and different types of social emancipation."

In Bangladesh, the Rana Plaza site is sometimes visited by foreign journalists and TV crews, who come to report on the updates. Roni Neaz, a Dhaka-based fixer, often joins them, but remains unconvinced that real change has filtered down. "There have been some infrastructural changes in factories since the tragedy – such as mending stairs and installing fire-safety gear – but people here are sceptical and worried that bribery might have prevented some closures. Also nothing has changed to help workers speak out. If a worker complains, he or she may be fired instantly." Technology, he feels, could speed things up. "That could be a weapon so the buyers are more responsible, workers have their freedom of expression and, technically, the owners will also be vigilant."

A few weeks after the Rana Plaza tragedy, Benetton tweeted a quasi-denial that spectacularly missed the point, saying that they had only placed a one-off order with one of

# Workers have had confidence to divulge sensitive information, including cases of sexual harassment and child labour

the manufacturers on the site and this was completed weeks prior to the accident. Since then an Italian documentary maker claims to have filmed another premises contracted by Benetton with no useable fire-exits. Benetton said it didn't recognise the building and that it continues to carry out random audits.

When campaigners first started exposing overseas sweatshops in the 1990s, some companies claimed they were shocked, that they struggled to monitor what was going on so far away. Those excuses didn't stand up then and they certainly don't now, not when there are so many lowcost ways to stay in touch and so much room for further innovation. As Franzese says: "In this globalised world, there is nowhere to hide." ☒

© Vicky Baker
www.indexoncensorship.org

**Vicky Baker** is deputy editor of Index on Censorship

www.tuyap.com.tr
35th Year

TÜRKİYE
YAYINCILAR
BİRLİĞİ
TURKISH PUBLISHERS ASSOCIATION

# 33rd İSTANBUL INTERNATIONAL

100 YEARS OF CINEMA IN TURKEY

ULUSLARARASI SALON 8-11 KASIM
INTERNATIONAL HALL NOVEMBER 8-11

**MACARİSTAN**
ONUR KONUĞU
**HUNGARY**
GUEST OF HONOR
Bir Bahçeden Bir Bahçeye
Egyik  Kertből  Másikba
*From One Garden to the Other*

## NOVEMBER 8-16, 2014

www.istanbulbookfair.com

kitapfuari

istanbulkitapfuari

kitapfuari

 KOSGEB
Supported By
 ufi The Global Association of the Exhibition Industry
Member
 ICCA International Congress and Convention Association
Member
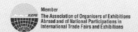 The Association of Organisers of Exhibitions Abroad and of National Participations in International Trade Fairs and Exhibitions
Member
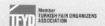 TFYD TURKISH FAIR ORGANIZERS ASSOCIATION
 TS EN ISO 9001:2008

 İSTANBUL

TÜYAP FAIR CONVENTION AND CONGRESS CENTER
Büyükçekmece, İstanbul / Turkey

# Index on Censorship
# on the go

**Find us in
the app store
today! A 30 day
subscription costs
just £1.79 and gives
you access to 6 years
of archived content.**

- Search current issue or archive
- Share pages instantly via e-mail, Twitter, Facebook and other social networks
- Pinch or double-tap pages to zoom
- Use animated thumbnail view to flick through pages
- Swipe page edges to flip to next/previous page
- Sync any issue to your device for offline reading (WiFi)
- Tap links to take you to websites, email addresses, references, maps…
- Tap contents-page links to jump to a particular article

## www.indexoncensorship.org/subscribe